How It Is Nowadays

Theodore Clymer

Priscilla Holton Fenn

Consultants

William E. Blanton EVALUATION

Milton D. Jacobson READABILITY

Ken Johnson LANGUAGE

Roger W. Shuy LINGUISTICS

E. Paul Torrance CREATIVITY

READING 720 READING 720
READING 720
GINN
READING 720
READING 720 READING 720

GINN AND COMPANY
A Xerox Education Company

Acknowledgments

Grateful acknowledgment is made to the following publishers, authors, and agents for permission to use and adapt copyrighted materials:

Frank Bonham for his story "A Pet Named Jet."

Clyde Robert Bulla for his story "The Invitation."

Vida Lindo Guiterman for the poem "Habits of the Hippopotamus" from *Gaily the Troubadour* by Arthur Guiterman. Published by permission of Vida Lindo Guiterman who owns the copyright.

Holt, Rinehart and Winston, Inc., for the poem beginning "The dark gray clouds, . . ." From *The Sun is a Golden Earring* by Natalia M. Belting. Copyright ©1962 by Natalia M. Belting. Reprinted by permission of Holt, Rinehart and Winston, Inc.

David McKay Company, Inc., for the adaptation of "The Donkey Egg." Copyright 1943 by A. G. Kelsey. From the book, *Once the Hodja* by A. G. Kelsey. Published by Longmans Green and Company. Used with permission of the David McKay Company.

Harriette H. Miller for her stories "Flossie Flamingo" and "William's Wish," for her play "The Three Spinning Fairies," and for her poems "The Adventures of Michael McGee" and "Christopher, the Contrary Chameleon."

Katherine Q. Morton for her story "Special Visitors."

Maurice O'Connell, Jr., for "The Tutor" by Carolyn Wells. Used by permission.

G. P. Putnam's Sons for the poem "Cookout Night." Reprinted by permission of G. P. Putnam's Sons from *Is Anybody Hungry?* by Dorothy Aldis. Copyright ©1964 by Dorothy Aldis.

Cynthia Stone Richmond for her stories "Dippy's Day by Moonlight" and "Fun for Maria."

Dorothy S. Thomas for her story "The Handre."

The Viking Press, Inc., for the poem "Firefly," from *Under the Tree* by Elizabeth Madox Roberts. Copyright 1922 by B. W. Huebsch, Inc. Copyright 1950 by Ivor S. Roberts. Reprinted by permission of The Viking Press, Inc.

Charlotte Zolotow for her story "The Farmer's Hut."

Acknowledgment for helpful advice is made to the following scientists: Dr. Tom Helliwell, Dr. Jon Mathews, Dr. Samuel Neff, and Dr. John S. Shelton.

Illustrations and photographs were provided by the following:
Ray Ameijide (208–219); Kathy Anderson (88–98); Willi Baum (220–235); Mark Bellerose (78–83); Ray Cruz (133–142); Faith Cushing (112 and 163); Bernard D'Andrea (8–18); John DeCindas (198–203); Sue Gernes (19–29); Les Gray (236); Trina Hyman (70–77); Susan Jeffers (57–62); Gordon Laite (237–243); Donald Leake (30–43); Alan Mardon (99–111); David McPhail (121–123); Carol L. Mullin (113–120); NASA (194); Nickzad Noujami (183); Joan Paley (168–174 and 184–189); Ted Rand (143–152) George Ulrich (44, 57–62, 63–69, 125, 165, 204, 205, 244 and 245); Christine Westerberg (128–132); Hans Zander (153–162)

The cover and unit introduction pages were designed by Gregory Fossella Associates.

Contents

4

Roosters, Rockets, and Wishes

7

THE FARMER'S HUT

Once there was a farmer.

He lived in one room of his small hut
with his wife and her mother
and his three small children.

He worked hard on his farm all day.
When he came home at night,
the noises in his house drove him crazy.

His wife talked to him.
His mother-in-law talked to him.
His three small children talked to him.
And they all talked at the same time!

The poor farmer put his hands
over his ears and cried,
"Please, please, QUIET, please!"
But they went right
on talking.

8

At last, in desperation,
he asked the advice of a wise man.

"What shall I do?" he asked.
"The noise is driving me crazy!"

"Will you follow my advice?"
the wise man asked.

"Yes," said the farmer.

"Good," the wise man said.
"Go home and bring
one cow into the house with you."

"A cow in the house!"
cried the farmer.
"How could that help?"

"Well, if you don't want my
advice . . . ," the wise man said.

9

So the farmer went home
and brought the cow into his house.

"A cow in the house!" said his wife.

"A cow in the house!"
said his mother-in-law.

"A cow in the house!"
said the children.

And they all said it at once.

"Moooooooo," said the cow,
bewildered by the noise.

The poor man just held his head.

"Quiet, please, QUIET, all of you!"
he cried.

The next day he went back
to the wise man.

"Well," said the wise man,
"how is it?"

"Worse than ever,"
said the farmer.

"While they talk,
the cow moos.
It's terrible!"

"Good," said the wise man.
"You have a dog?"

"Yes," said the farmer,
"two of them."

"Good," said the wise man.
"Tonight bring the dogs
into the house too."

"Bring the dogs into the house!"
shouted the farmer.

"Well—if you don't want
my advice . . . ," said the wise man.

11

So the farmer went home
and brought the two dogs into the house too.

"A cow and two dogs!" said his wife.

"A cow and two dogs in the house!"
said his mother-in-law.

"A cow and two dogs in the house!"
said the children.

"Moooooooo," said the bewildered cow.

And the two dogs barked
at being locked up inside.

The poor farmer just held his head.

"Quiet, please, all of you,"
        he moaned.

The next day the farmer went back
to the wise man.

"How is it now?" the wise man asked.

"Worse, worse than ever," said the farmer.

"Are you sure you know what you are doing?"

"Yes," said the wise man.
"Tonight I want you to be sure to
bring indoors your rooster and all the hens."

"My rooster and all the hens!"
cried the farmer. "How will that help?"

"Well—if you don't want
my advice . . . ," the wise man said.

So the farmer went home
and brought his rooster and
all the hens into his house.

"A cow, two dogs, a rooster
and all these hens in the house!"
said. his wife. "Are you crazy?"

"A cow, two dogs, a rooster
and all these hens!" said his
mother-in-law. "Are you crazy?"

"A cow, two dogs, a rooster,
and all our hens!" cried the children.

"Moooooooo . .," went the cow.

"Werf werf werf," went the dogs.

"Cackledecackle decackle," went
the hens while the rooster crowed.

"Quiet," moaned the poor man.
"Oh, quiet."

14

The next day the farmer went back to the wise man.

"How is it?" the wise man asked.

"Terrible," said the farmer,
"terrible. I cannot last another night like this."

"All right," said the wise man.
"Now listen with care. Tonight,
go home and be sure to put the cow
back in the barn."

The farmer did, and while there
was still a lot of noise, at least the
cow was not there to moo at him.

The following night
he went to the wise man again.

"How was it?" the wise man asked.

"Better," the farmer said,
"better than the night before."

"Good," the wise man said.
"Tonight go back and be sure to put out
the two dogs."

15

And that night there was a lot
of noise. But at least there was
no cow mooing and no dogs barking.
"How was it?" the wise man
asked the next night.
"Better," the man said.
"Fine," the wise man said.
"Tonight go home and put out
the rooster and the hens."
And the farmer did.
No cow mooed at him.
No dogs barked.
No rooster crowed.
No hens cackled.
It was wonderful !

16

Next night he went back
to the wise man.

"How is it now?" the wise man asked.

"Last night it was wonderful," the farmer
said, "so quiet, so quiet,

no mooing,

no barking,

no crowing,

no cackling.

IT'S WONDERFUL—JUST WONDERFUL!

17

"Good," said the wise man,
"I told you it would be better."
And the farmer went home.
His wife and mother-in-law
and three children said,
"At last, you have come
to your senses again."
But he only smiled to himself.
For without the cow
and the two dogs,
and the rooster,
and the hens,
their voices seemed very quiet indeed.

"INDEED!"

Flossie Flamingo

Flossie Flamingo flew back to Florida to spend the winter. Right away she knew things had changed. Not far from the marsh where she lived, a huge round pointed thing jutted into the air.

Flossie said to her friend, Olive Owl, who knew everything, "How things have changed around here! What is that big tall thing?"

"It's a rocket," said Olive.

"It looks like a big silo," said Flossie. "I once stayed near a farm with a silo. Are you sure it isn't a silo?"

"Yes, I'm sure," said Olive Owl. "I flew over and listened to the men talking when they were building it. They said it was a rocket. They said it was going to—"

"It's a rocket-silo," Flossie decided. "Yes, I'm sure that's what it is." And home she went.

Day after day Flossie Flamingo flew past the rocket-silo. After a while she saw it so often she hardly noticed it.

Then early one morning, she did notice smoke at the base of the rocket-silo.

"Where there's smoke there's fire!" she cried.

Sure enough, red flames shot out with a roar.

"The rocket-silo is burning up!" yelled Flossie Flamingo, but it was so early that no one heard her.

Flossie could hardly believe her eyes. Slowly at first, and then faster and faster, the rocket-silo was lifted into the air. Trailing smoke and fire, it roared out of sight, leaving Flossie's ears ringing.

"How terrible! The rocket-silo has torn a great hole in the sky," cried Flossie. "Who would believe it! Soon all the stars will fall through! I must find a safe place to hide."

She flapped over to an old log. Standing on one foot, she tucked her head under her wing and shut her eyes.

Soon her friend, Hilda Heron, flew by the old log and noticed Flossie.

"Why, Flossie Flamingo," said Hilda. "Why are you asleep so early in the day?"

"I'm not asleep," said Flossie, lifting her wing a little and looking out from under it. "Everything's changed around here. I'm hiding, and you'd better hide too! The rocket-silo tore a great big hole in the sky, and all the stars are going to fall out."

"How terrible!" said Hilda Heron. "How did you find out about it?"

"I saw it! I heard it!" cried Flossie. "Quick! Find a safe place."

So Hilda Heron crouched beside Flossie Flamingo and put her head under her wing.

23

In a little while Katy Crane flew by and saw Flossie and Hilda.

"What are you doing down there?" she called as she floated down for a landing.

"We're hiding," said Hilda Heron. "And you'd better hide too. Have you noticed the sky? The rocket-silo tore a big hole in it and all the stars are going to fall out."

"How terrible!" said Katy Crane. "How did you find out about it?"

"Flossie Flamingo told me," said Hilda.

"Yes, yes," said Flossie. "Early this morning I saw it! I heard it! Hurry! Find yourself a safe place."

So Katy Crane got very close to Hilda Heron and put her head under her wing.

24

A little later Rachel Rail flew by. She saw Flossie and Hilda and Katy, and she landed with a thud.

"Are you having a party?" asked Rachel.

"No," said Katy Crane. "We're hiding and you'd better hide too. The rocket-silo tore a great hole in the sky, and any time now all the stars will come falling through."

"How terrible!" said Rachel Rail. "How did you find out about it?"

"Hilda Heron told me," said Katy Crane.

"Flossie told me," said Hilda Heron.

"Yes, yes," said Flossie Flamingo, poking her bill out from under her wing. "I saw it! I heard it! Hurry! Find a safe place."

So Rachel Rail crowded close beside Katy Crane, and there the four of them stayed for the rest of the day.

Then after it was dark, Olive Owl came flying by looking for her dinner.

"How strange!" she said when she saw the four birds crouched side by side on the log. "What are you doing here after dark?"

"We're hiding," said Rachel Rail, "and you'd better hide too."

"For goodness sake, why?" asked Olive Owl.

"There's going to be a terrible change," added Katy Crane. "Any second now all the stars will fall through. You'd better believe it!"

"How did you find out about all this?" asked Olive Owl.

"Flossie Flamingo told us," said Hilda.

"Yes, yes," said Flossie in a hushed voice from under her wing. "I saw it! I heard it! Quick! Find a safe place."

"My tree is safe enough for me," said Olive Owl. "But right now I'm going to find some dinner."

"What? What?" said the others. "Aren't you going to hide? What about the rocket-silo?"

"I don't know about a rocket-silo." said Olive Owl. "But I do know a rocket left for the moon early this morning. I watched it go."

"But the hole in the sky!" said Flossie Flamingo.

"Open your eyes and look," said Olive Owl.

Slowly they all took their heads from under their wings and looked up. There were the stars, all in their same places. Nothing had changed.

"Oh," said Flossie Flamingo. "I guess the stars aren't going to fall after all."

"I guess not," said the others.

"I guess not!" said Olive Owl.

Cookout Night

Paper cups and paper plates.

Pickles in a pickle jar.

Popcorn in a crackly bag.

Salt and pepper?

Here they are.

Paper napkins! Who forgot?

"I didn't, you did."

"I did *not*.

Besides, what difference does it make?

Look at all the grass around

For wiping hands and faces on . . ."

Nothing's ever impolite:

Not outdoors on cookout night.

Dorothy Aldis

29

William's Wish

1. BIRTHDAY CANDLES

It was William's birthday. He was having a party with his family and six of his best friends. Because his birthday was in August, and the weather was nice and warm, the party was in William's back yard. There were games of "Balloon Tag" and "Peanut Hunt," and there were hot dogs and slices of ice-cold watermelon to eat. After that, William opened his gifts. Last of all, when it was almost dark, Mother brought out a big cake with seven candles.

"Make a wish, William," said Dad.

"You have to blow out all the candles at once," said his friend Mark.

"That's right," said Mother. "If you do, you'll get your wish before your next birthday."

"Take a deep breath," said Mrs. Brooks, who lived next door.

"Close your eyes," said William's sister Julie.

William took a deep breath and closed his eyes.

"Now BLOW!" said everyone all at once.

William blew, and out went every one of the candles.

"Good for you," said Mother. "Now you'll get your wish."

"I hope so," said William, "because I wished—"

"Don't tell!" interrupted Julie. "If you tell, your wish won't come true."

"That's right," Mrs. Brooks agreed.

"I won't tell," said William. "But how long do I wait for my wish to come true? Till it's time for another birthday party?"

"It could be soon," Mrs. Brooks said.

"Or take a whole year," suggested Julie.

William sighed. "A whole year. That's fall, winter, spring, and summer again. A whole year is a long time to wait for a wish."

For the rest of the summer and the first part of fall William waited, and he didn't tell his wish. Then school started. It was fun to walk home with Mark and cross the busy highway at the corner.

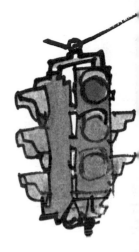

One fall afternoon William and Mark were waiting for the light to turn green, when they saw a big truck with a load of hay. William saw Mark close his eyes, lick his thumb, and pound his right fist into his left hand.

"What're you doing?" asked William.

"Making a wish," said Mark. "Everyone knows that's how you wish on a load of hay."

"I didn't know it," said William. "I could have been making a wish too."

"Not on that load of hay, because—"

"Why not?" interrupted William.

"You have to wish as soon as you see it. If you talk first, it's no good. And you can't look back."

"Does it work?" asked William. "I mean, does your wish really come true?"

"I never kept track," said Mark. "Come on. The light's changed to green."

WILLIAM KEEPS WISHING

That night William told Julie about making a wish on a load of hay.

"It would have been fun to try it," he said. "And my birthday wish may really come true faster if I keep making the wish."

"You could make a new wish," suggested Julie.

"A new wish?" William thought about it. Then he sighed, "I don't think I'll make a new wish till I get my birthday wish."

"Why not?" asked Julie.

"Well, today Mark said he never kept track of his wishes. Did you ever keep track?"

"No, not really," said Julie.

"Well, I think I'll just keep wishing that same birthday wish. That way I'll know."

35

It was nearly a week before William saw a load of hay, but he remembered to lick his thumb and pound his left hand with his right fist. Then he took a deep breath and wished his birthday wish. He didn't look back.

All that fall William waited, but he didn't tell his wish. He wished again when he and Julie snapped the Thanksgiving turkey wishbone. William got the long end of it, but when winter came, his wish still hadn't come true.

2. STARS AND EYELASHES

One clear winter evening William went out to get the newspaper. It wasn't quite dark but already he could see one bright star. William looked hard at the star and chanted softly,

"Star light, star bright,
First star I've seen tonight,
I wish I may, I wish I might
Have the wish I wish tonight."

Once again he wished his birthday wish.

Back inside he gave Dad the paper and said, "I just wished on the evening star."

"Where did you hear of that?"

"I don't know," said William. "I guess everyone knows about wishing on a star."

Julie looked up from her homework. "You can wish on shooting stars too," she said. "Only you don't see them often."

"I've never seen one," sighed William, "but I'll look for them from now on."

All through the winter William looked for shooting stars, and he waited, and he didn't tell his birthday wish. One day he learned about wishing on a white horse. By spring William had wished on three white horses, but hadn't seen one shooting star, and his wish hadn't come true.

Then one bright windy afternoon
William opened the front door
and called, "Hi, Mom! I'm home
from school!"

"Already?" said Mom giving him a
hug. Then she stopped, really looked
at his face, and said, "Hold still,
you've got an eyelash."

"I've got a whole bunch of them."

"I know, but this one's loose. Here. Get
it on your hand and you can make a wish.
It might come true," said his mother.

"On an eyelash? I never heard of that."

"You close your eyes, and wish, and blow.
If your eyelash is gone, you know it went to
make your wish come true."

"Do wishes really come true, Mom?"

"Some people say they do," Mom answered.

"I never get my wishes," William said with a sigh. "I've already wished that same wish over and over. I'm tired of wishing it."

William looked at the eyelash on his hand, closed his eyes, wished his birthday wish, and blew as hard as he could. When he looked, the eyelash was gone.

"If that eyelash really went to get my wish," he said, "I sure hope it hurries!"

A few weeks later Mrs. Brooks showed him how to wish on the first robin of spring, but when spring was over, William's wish still hadn't come true.

DO WISHES COME TRUE?

Then summer came. On the Fourth of July William's family went to the fireworks show at the park. They sat for a long, long time waiting for it to get dark, but when the first bright skyrocket burst in the air William forgot the long wait. Every "firework" lit the sky in a shower of shooting stars. William wasn't sure they were the right kind of shooting stars, but he wished and wished.

The next day Mom said, "We're finally getting some warm July weather. Let's eat outdoors tonight."

That evening, after William had finished his second hot dog and his third slice of watermelon, he sat down on the lawn. Julie sat beside him and picked a dandelion stem with a fuzzy ball at the end.

"Here," she said. "You can blow on this and make a wish."

41

"No, thanks," said William.

"You shouldn't give up just because you didn't get your birthday wish," said Julie.

"I'm not giving up," said William. "I finally got my wish."

"You did?"

"Sure. I got it tonight. I wished we'd eat outdoors and have hot dogs and watermelon, and tonight we did," William said.

"You mean that's what you've been wishing for nearly a year?" asked Julie.

William nodded.

"Well, didn't your wish come true?"

"Sure," said William. "But maybe all my wishes didn't matter. I don't think I really believe in wishes."

"I don't, either. I just half-believe," said Julie, as she went to get more watermelon.

It wasn't quite dark, but just over the back fence William could see one bright star in the clear July sky. Softly he began to chant,

"Star light, star bright . . .

I wish I may, I wish I might . . ."

Riddles

I live in Florida.
I am a big bird.
My feathers are pink.
I am _____.

I am also a bird.
I fly at night.
Some people call me wise.
I am _____.

William made a wish on me.
I am up in the sky.
You can see me at night.
I am _____.

Six people live in me.
I am one room.
Animals have also lived in me.
I am _____.

Yes or No

Explain your answers.
1. Can you mail a flamingo in an envelope?
2. When you wish on an eyelash, does your wish always come true?
3. Is a whole year spring, summer, and winter?
4. Do flamingoes hide their heads under their wings?
5. Is a rocket-silo like a submarine?
6. Is a turkey dinner special for the 4th of July?
7. Can you wish on a yellow dandelion?
8. Is the mother of the farmer's wife his mother-in-law?
9. Are shooting stars the same as fireworks?
10. Is a small hut a good place to keep farm animals?

44

Scrambled Sentences

Read the words in each row in the correct
order to make a sentence.

The Farmer's Hut

1. had   The   one   hut   only   room   farmer's
2. of   The   noise   lot   animals   made   a
3. drove   The   noise   farmer   crazy   the
4. man   The   wise   a   asked   from   advice   farmer

Flossie Flamingo

1. The   thing   tall   a   looked   like   silo
2. noticed   Flossie   it   while   a   hardly   After
3. rocket   morning   the   the   left   One   moon   for
4. rocket-silo   hole   a   the   torn   in   The   sky   has

William's Wish

1. for   many   wished   William   something   times
2. kept   whole   William   year   a   wishing   for
3. made   on   star   William   a   one   bright   wish
4. eat   William's   outdoors   to   was   wish

Now scramble some sentences on your own, and
try them on a friend.

Very Special Friends

47

Speck

Spring was coming to Tait Primary School. On the new highway big trucks went by the school all day. And new red, green, and yellow signals were ready at the school crossing. The girls and boys in Miss Day's class were talking about them.

"I'm sure you know how to obey the new signals, don't you?" Miss Day asked.

Mark Zapella answered. "First we check the lights. Green, red, or yellow. We know about them. But now we watch for the new signal that says W-A-L-K. Then we obey it and go across the highway, and we stay inside the crosswalk lines."

Everyone nodded but Ben. He was thinking about his dog, Speck.

Ann Dines added something. "My mother meets me every day after school. She doesn't want me to cross the highway without her."

"Why not?" Mark asked. "All we have to do is obey the new signals."

The children talked and Miss Day listened. Finally she asked Ben a question, "What do you think about obeying signals?"

Ben said, "I was thinking about my dog, Speck. He obeys."

Speck was Ben's new Springer Spaniel. His coat was white with black specks in it. He could do tricks. He could catch a ball. He could stand on his hind legs and beg. He knew how to obey signals.

"How many signals can Speck obey?" Miss Day asked.

Ben named them. "When my Dad says 'Come,' Speck comes. When Dad says 'Heel,' Speck walks along beside him. He says 'Stay!' and Speck stays where he is until Dad tells him to move. Oh, Speck obeys signals all right."

Ann asked another question, "Does he obey you?"

"Yes," Ben said. "I'm his master now, and he's just learned how to fetch."

"How does he fetch?" asked Ann.

"Well, my baby sister creeps everywhere now. Sometimes she goes too far away. I call Speck and point to the baby. I say 'Fetch!' and Speck races to her. He pulls at her dress with his teeth. He doesn't tear her dress. He never bites her. He just pulls her back to me. Then I give him a special biscuit. That special biscuit makes him happy and . . ."

Mark Zapella interrupted, "Can you bring Speck to school so we can see him fetch?"

Ben said, "I can't bring my baby sister too, but I could bring her doll and show you. That's how I trained Speck. He learned to fetch with the doll."

"May I bring my little sister to watch Speck?" Ann Dines asked. "Little Jenny needs to learn to obey too."

Ben did bring Speck to school one afternoon, and Ann brought Little Jenny for this special time.

Speck obeyed every command that Ben gave him.

"Fetch!" Ben commanded. He pointed to the doll. All the children watched Speck, especially Jenny.

Speck skidded across the schoolroom floor to the doll. He clamped his teeth into her dress. With great care he pulled her back to his master.

Jenny laughed and laughed.

After school Ben took Speck out to the school crosswalk near the new signals. His father was going to meet them there.

"Sit!" Ben commanded, and Speck obeyed. He sat very upright, close to his master's feet. Ben watched the highway for his father's truck. It was time for it to come.

Ann Dines came out with Jenny to wait for their mother.

"Sit, stay, fetch!" Jenny commanded Speck, but the dog did not move.

Ben wished the truck would come. Jenny was a pest.

Then Ben heard a horn. His father's truck was moving slowly toward the crosswalk.

Jenny began to jump up and down. "Over there! Over there! There's Mommy!"

Across the highway at the other end of the crosswalk Mrs. Dines was waiting. The signal light was red, and Jenny's mother was signaling her to wait with Ann.

The truck was rolling closer. Jenny did not notice the truck or the red light or her mother's signaling. Before Ann could stop her, Jenny darted out into the crosswalk.

Ben saw her. He bent down and pointed to Jenny. "FETCH HER!" he commanded.

In one bound Speck had Jenny by her shirt. He gave a quick hard pull, and Jenny landed on the curb again. She was screaming, but she was safe.

The truck had stopped. The brakes had been strong enough to hold. Ben's father jumped out of the truck and hurried over to the children.

Ann helped Jenny stand up, and she put her arms around her little sister. Jenny stopped screaming and watched Ben and Speck.

Ben was patting Speck. "Good dog, good dog," he kept saying as he pulled out a special biscuit. "Sit!" he ordered. "Stay!" Speck obeyed the commands, and Ben gave him the biscuit.

Now the crosswalk signal said W-A-L-K. Mrs. Dines hurried across the highway. "Oh, Jenny!" she cried. "That dog saved you."

Speck just sat upright beside his master and chewed his biscuit.

Roady Roadrunner And Yoshi

Roady Roadrunner lived in the high desert. His house was a prickly bush by the side of the road. Yoshi lived in the high desert too. Every morning on her way to school Yoshi passed Roady's house, and he always ran out of the bush to greet her.

Roady had strong legs for running, and a long strong tail. The tail stayed out straight behind him when he ran. When he stopped running, his tail would stand straight up. It was like a brake. It helped Roady to make a quick stop.

One morning when Roady ran to meet Yoshi, he sang a strange song. It sounded a little like a cuckoo, because Roady belonged to the cuckoo family. He sang the song, and then he cocked his head.

Yoshi stood and looked at him. "If I could run as fast as you run," she said, "I could be on time for school. I am late every day."

Roady ran ahead of Yoshi and made a quick stop at a fork in the road. He braked his run with his strong tail. Then he stood there, waiting for Yoshi.

At the fork one road went on in a straight line to the school. It was the best way to go. It was the shorter way.

Yoshi did not go the shorter way. On that road a big black dog lived. He barked at her. He was very strong, and one day he had pushed her down. She was afraid of him.

The other road was longer. Yoshi went that way to school. She hurried. Sometimes she ran. But she was always late for school because that way took longer.

Her teacher, Mr. Pine, always looked upset when she came in late. Today he said, "Yoshi, you are late again! Please promise to be on time tomorrow. Why is it that you are always late?"

Yoshi stood with her head down and could not answer. If she told about the dog, the children would laugh at her.

At closing time Mr. Pine said, "Promise to be on time tomorrow, Yoshi. Please try."

"I will try," she said softly. "I promise."

The next morning Roady Roadrunner did not run out to meet Yoshi. She heard a whirring buz-z-z-z in the bush. It sounded like a rattlesnake.

Yoshi looked behind the bush. There was Roady, and there was a small rattlesnake. It was ready to strike Roady!

But Roady did not run away on his strong fast legs. He ran straight at the little snake. The snake missed its strike, and Roady pecked at its head. Then Roady jumped back and stopped where the snake could not strike him. He was ready to run at it again.

Roady was in danger. He was a brown bird, all alone. He did not run away, but the snake did. It found a rock and crawled under it.

Yoshi ran back to the road, but Roady was there first. He cocked his head and gave her his greeting.

Yoshi bowed. "You are a brave bird," she said. "You are really strong."

Then she started to go on to school.

Roady ran ahead to the fork of the road. He braked his tail and looked at her and sang his cooing song.

"Are you telling me not to be afraid?" Yoshi asked the bird as she came to the place where the road forked.

She looked down the shorter road to the school and saw the dog lying there. She looked at Roady and remembered how bravely he had faced the snake.

Yoshi took a big breath. "I can look after myself too," she said. And she took the shorter way.

She walked right by the dog. It growled a little, but she did not stop. The dog did not bark. It did not get up.

"I guess you know me this time," Yoshi said. She walked straight ahead to school. Mr. Pine smiled when he saw her. "You remembered your promise. You're on time!"

Yoshi looked straight at Mr. Pine. She said, "Roady Roadrunner helped me."

Aquí Está Mi Nieta

Ana Rosa had come to stay with her grandmother in the United States and go to school there. On the first morning Grandmother walked to school with Ana Rosa. They were speaking in Spanish. At school Ana Rosa would speak English and learn some new words.

"You will find new friends here, Ana Rosa," her grandmother said. "They will help you with the new English words."

Ana Rosa nodded. She was looking at the tall flagpole in front of the school. Two boys were raising the flag.

Her grandmother called to one of them, "Eduardo, aquí está mi nieta!"

[1]Aquí Está Mi Nieta (ah·KEE e·STAH MEE NEAY·tah)

Eduardo ran to meet them. He spoke to Ana Rosa in English. "Hi! Let's go to our room. Everyone wants to see you!"

To her grandmother he said, "I'll show her the way home after school." And he led Ana Rosa to the classroom.

The teacher said, "Welcome, Ana Rosa." "Why don't you sit at Eduardo's table?" she suggested. "Then he can help you."

"Thank you," said Ana Rosa.

Everyone was smiling at her. These new friends were giving her a good welcome.

"Oh," she thought as she listened to the new sounds,

"it's easy

to understand."

Just before closing time the teacher said, "Let's go out to the playground to show Ana Rosa what we know about our shadows."

"Let's show her where her shadow is when the afternoon sun is behind her in the west," someone suggested.

"I'll trace her shadow on a long sheet of paper," Eduardo said.

Ana Rosa did not know the English word "shadow," so she did not understand the talk. And why was everyone going outdoors?

65

At a sunny spot on the sidewalk Eduardo said, "Turn your back to the sun, Ana Rosa." He pointed in the right direction.

He unrolled the paper on the walk in front of her feet. With a big black marker he traced the outline of her shadow. It was almost as long as the sheet of paper.

The children pointed in the direction of the sun. "There's the sun behind you in the west. Your shadow's in front of you. What does that tell you, Ana Rosa?" they asked.

Ana Rosa did not understand. The teacher tried to help her. "The sun is in the west in the afternoon, Ana Rosa. Your shadow helps to show you where the west is."

But no one helped Ana Rosa with the new English word "shadow." It was like being lost and not finding the way.

Eduardo understood. "Never mind," he suggested softly to her in Spanish. "On our way home your shadow will be in front of you. That's all you need to remember."

The school bell rang, and it was time to go home.

"Meet me at the flagpole," Eduardo said.

Ana Rosa said good-by to her new friends and walked to the flagpole.

The flag was gone, and so was Eduardo. Where was he? How could she find her way home? She stood on the front walk and waited. She looked in all directions. Everything looked strange.

She looked down at the sidewalk. Her own black shadow was in front of her feet. It was like finding a friend.

"My shadow," Ana Rosa said in Spanish. She said it again in English. And this time she remembered Eduardo's words.

Could the shadow lead her in the right direction? Could it lead Ana Rosa back to her grandmother's house?

Ana Rosa took a step forward. The shadow moved forward too. The sun was behind her. She walked on, finding a way while her shadow stayed in front of her. She let the shadow lead her until she heard Eduardo's voice behind her, calling, "Ana Rosa, wait for me!"

When he reached her, he pointed to a house just ahead of them. "There's your grandmother's house," he said. "You knew how to find your way alone, didn't you?"

"With my shadow to show me," Ana Rosa said, "it was easy!"

69

The Mystery of the Suitcase

Mrs. Emory lived in a little house. Her kitchen door looked out on tall trees. In the summer the kitchen door stood wide open.

Charles Workman lived in a big two-story house nearby. The Workman family were new in the neighborhood. Charles and Mrs. Emory had become good friends. He liked to sit on the steps outside her door and watch her make cookies.

Day after day Mrs. Emory made cookies in her kitchen. No one in the neighborhood knew why. Those cookies were a mystery. But Charles did know what kind of cookies they were.

On Monday Mrs. Emory always made gingersnaps. Monday was a spicy day.

On Tuesday she baked brownies. The air around the kitchen was pretty sweet on Tuesday.

The next day she made peanut-butter cookies. Charles Workman liked these best.

Thursday cookies were never the same.

"Thursday is my leftover day," Mrs. Emory said.

And the last cooky day of each week was for Mrs. Emory's special, own crunchy oatmeal cookies.

On Saturday morning Mrs. Emory went off on a six o'clock bus. Where she went was a mystery. She took a heavy, old suitcase. She came home in the evening on a six o'clock bus. Then the suitcase was heavier.

Charles liked to carry the suitcase to the bus and carry it home again at night. Mrs. Emory always said, "Are you strong enough to carry the suitcase today? It's heavy."

He knew he was strong enough! At the bus he watched Mrs. Emory hop aboard. She was as quick as anything. Her hair was white. Her shoes were old and a little too big. Her coat was long, and so were her skirts. Her hat was green.

Charles handed the heavy suitcase up to her, and she handed him a bag. "Here is your pay, and thank you, Charles Workman. I don't aim to be beholden."

The pay was exactly the same every week—three Monday cookies, two Tuesday cookies, and one each for the other three days.

One Saturday night he waited and waited. "Mom," he called when he came home. "Mrs. Emory is never this late. I wonder where she is."

His mother said, "She's a mystery to me."

Charles shook his head, "I think Mrs. Emory takes those cookies somewhere special."

"Maybe she sells them," suggested his mother. "Are her cookies good enough to sell, Charles?"

"They sure are! I like them a lot and I like Mrs. Emory too. She is one of my best friends. But I do wonder what is making her so late today."

On Sunday morning Charles went over to the kitchen door and peeked in Mrs. Emory's window. The house seemed too still.

"I wonder where she can be?" he asked himself again. "There's no one here."

But behind him, he heard a man say, "Looking for something?" A strange policeman was looking at him.

"I am looking for Mrs. Emory," Charles told him. "She never says where she is going, but she always comes home at night. Her suitcase is very heavy then, and I help her carry it. Last night she never came."

The policeman made some notes in his book. Charles's father came hurrying across the garden. "What is going on here?" Mr. Workman asked.

The policeman answered, "Your son is worried about your neighbor. Quite a detective you have in your family, sir."

"Mrs. Emory? She comes and goes with her old, heavy suitcase. That's all we know about her. She is a neighborhood mystery."

"Oh, Dad," Charles cried. "She's my friend, and I do wonder where she is now!"

The policeman smiled. "She is spending a few days in the City Hospital. She is having a little rest in her other home."

How could a hospital be her home?

The policeman was saying, "Mrs. Emory worked in the hospital kitchen for a long time, making special cookies for children. They liked her cookies best of all."

"So she takes her cookies to children in the hospital. But why is that suitcase so heavy when she comes home?" Charles asked.

"That suitcase is full of special things for making more cookies. The hospital gives them to her," the policeman answered.

"Do they pay her for making the cookies?"

"No, indeed. She likes to do it for the children," the policeman said. "When she needs a rest, she uses a hospital room. She'll be home soon, as lively as ever."

Charles said slowly, "She's going to need me. I'll be waiting for her so I can carry that suitcase. Please tell her I'll be ready."

Fun for Maria

Sharon stood in the doorway of her grandfather's house. She looked across the valley. How different it was from the city.

Here on the Indian reservation the only sounds were from the birds and the wind. The nearest house was two miles away. It was land her family had lived on for many, many years.

Right now Grandfather was working in his fine garden. Sharon's mother had gone to visit an old friend. She would be away all morning. What is there for me to do, Sharon wondered.

Then she noticed the little burro standing in the field. "May I take Maria a carrot?" she asked her grandfather.

"Nothing to stop you," he said.

Sharon took the carrot and went down the path to the field. The burro looked up. She pointed her long ears at Sharon. Sharon fed her the carrot. She stroked the soft fur of the burro's ears. Maria finished the carrot and nudged Sharon.

"So you want to go," laughed Sharon. Maria was tied to a stake in the ground. Sharon untied the rope. Then, standing on a rock, she climbed onto the burro's back.

"Maria and I are going to hunt for pine needles. I will make baskets," she called to her grandfather.

They headed up the mountain. Soon Sharon saw acorns on the ground. She knew her ancestors made bread from acorns in the old days. She slid off Maria's back. She filled her pockets with acorns.

After a while they came out into an open meadow. They went very slowly. Maria kept finding things to eat. Finally, Sharon stopped. She sat down on a big rock.

In the rock were some small holes. "That's where Indians used to grind their acorns," she told Maria.

She put some acorns in one hole. Then she hunted for a rock to pound them with. Pounding took two hands. She let go of the rope. "Don't wander away," she told Maria.

Grinding the acorns was hard work. Her arms grew tired. And oh, how hot she was! She stopped to rest and looked around for Maria. The burro was nowhere to be seen. "Maria!" she called. "Maria!"

Sharon climbed to the top of the big rock. She looked and listened. There was no sign of the burro. But strange sounds seemed to be all around her.

"I'm all alone," she whispered. She closed her eyes and shook. Then she opened them again.

Something was moving on the far side of the clearing. Could it be a wildcat? What made the leaves rustle so? Was it a snake? Everything looked and sounded strange and scary. She wanted to be home, even without Maria. She wasn't sure where home was. But she had to get there.

She turned and ran. The ground was very rough. Soon she knew that this was not the way they had come.

Suddenly she stepped on a loose stone and fell down. For a while she lay on the ground. Her knee stung. She felt like crying. She wanted to stay there. But she knew she must get home. She also knew she was lost. What should she do?

As Sharon lay there, she suddenly heard the sound of hoofs. She sat up. There came the burro, with her ears pointed. Maria reached Sharon and nudged her with her nose.

"Oh, Maria, I thought I'd lost you. And here you've found me."

Sharon got to her feet. She picked up the rope. She led the burro to a rock, and climbed onto her back. Without even a small kick, Maria started off. But not the way Sharon had been going. She headed the other way. Sharon said nothing.

Around the side of a hill and through some trees they went. Suddenly they came out into the open. There, next to a field of corn, was Grandfather's house.

All of Sharon's fears left her. And she forgot all about her knee. She yelled. There, standing on the porch, were her mother and grandfather. How wonderful it was to be home!

"What on earth have you been doing?" her mother asked.

"I've been making acorn bread like my ancestors. And Maria had fun helping me," Sharon answered. "But we didn't find any pine needles," she added.

Her grandfather's eyes twinkled, but he asked no questions.

Take the Right Road

Help the roadrunner find the rattlesnake. Follow only the road that has on it words with the same vowel sounds as in *bite* and *head*. Watch the forks in the road. If you take a wrong turn, go back and try another road.

Begin with the roadrunner and the word *bite*. You must end at the snake and the word *head*.

Think of a New Ending

Speck

Tell how Speck might have acted at the end of the story if Ben hadn't trained him to "fetch."

Roady Roadrunner and Yoshi

How might the story have been different if Yoshi had not fed the roadrunner and made a pet of it?

Aquí Está Mi Nieta

If Ana Rosa had not learned about the sun and her shadow, how might the story have ended?

The Mystery of the Suitcase

How would the story change if no one knew where Mrs. Emory was?

Fun for Maria

What might have happened to Sharon if the burro had not known the way back home?

86

Opening New Doors

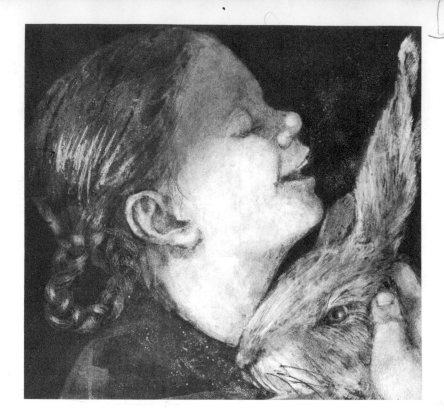

LAURA'S WORLD

This is the true story of Laura Bridgman. When she was two years old, she was very ill. She could not see or hear or talk. Her world was dark and very small.

Three people helped her very much. One was Uncle Asa. He was a friend of the Bridgman family. Another was her mother. The other was Dr. Howe. He worked with children in a school for the blind.

I.

Laura had to learn how to make her wants and feelings known. How could she show that she was thirsty or that she wanted someone to come to her? How could she show that she was happy?

One way was to make signs with her hands. She put her hand to her mouth as if tipping a cup. That meant "drink." She pulled her hand toward her. That meant "come." Pushing her hand away meant "go." A pat on the head meant she liked someone or something. A pat on the back meant she did not like someone or something.

Another early lesson was learning more about the world around her. Her first teacher was Uncle Asa. He was an old man who loved her very much. He helped her use her sense of touch. She could not see or hear or talk, but she could feel.

When she was very little, she loved to have Uncle Asa carry her about in his arms. She loved the warm sunlight and the cool woods. She loved to go down by the river.

Laura could not see the sun, but she could feel its warmth. She could not hear the trees rustle, but she could feel the wind. She could not see the shining water or hear its soft sounds. But she could feel the cool water with her hands. She loved to throw stones into the water, even though she could not see them sail through the air or hear them splash.

When she could walk, she and Uncle Asa wandered over fields and through woods together. These morning walks were her school. She learned about living things even though she could not see them.

Uncle Asa often walked with Laura to the barn. She liked hunting for the hens' nests. She liked putting her hand into the nest to find eggs. She knew that she must be very gentle and leave one egg for each hen.

Another time Uncle Asa brought her a little rabbit. She patted its soft fur. She felt its long ears. She smiled when its cool nose moved over her arm.

Laura learned to feel the soft wool of a lamb, and the smooth sleekness of a horse. Though Laura did not know the names of living things, she did know their shape and how they felt.

Her sense of touch became a doorway for her. Through it she could go into the world around her.

At home, Laura also learned the feel of things as she helped her mother. She learned the shape of plates and knives and forks.

She knew where everyone sat. She gave each one the right things. The two small plates always went to her two little brothers. She knew her own tin plate by the decorations around the rim. She could feel the decorations. Only later did she learn that they were letters.

II.

Laura had a tool with which she could learn. In place of eyes and ears, she could use her sense of touch.

Just before her eighth birthday Laura went to a special school for the blind. Young Dr. Howe had never before known a child who was blind and could not hear or talk. He said,

"She is in a room without light. How can she find the way out into the world?" And so Dr. Howe started to help her.

This was the way her first lesson began.

Dr. Howe printed on slips of paper the names of some of the things Laura knew by touch. There were such words as KNIFE, FORK, KEY, CHAIR, and DOOR. The words were in raised letters that she could feel. There were two slips for each word. One he pasted on the thing it named. The other he placed in Laura's hand.

First Dr. Howe had Laura feel the word KNIFE on the slip of paper. She moved her fingers over it until she had felt all the letters and knew their shapes. Then he gave her the knife and had her feel the letters on its label.

He helped her understand that the two sets of letters were the same. He placed his two forefingers side by side. That meant that two things were alike. Her smile showed that she understood.

Dr. Howe then did the same with the other things. First the fork, then the key, then the chair, and then the door. Each time her fingers felt the shape of the letters on the label. Then she felt the shape of the letters on the paper.

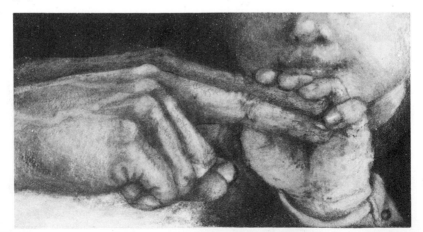

Laura understood that the raised letters on the knife and on the paper were the same. KNIFE and KNIFE were the same. And so were CHAIR and CHAIR.

Dr. Howe had Laura feel the raised letters on the label of one thing. Then those on the label of another thing. KNIFE and FORK did not feel the same. DOOR and CHAIR were different.

Laura soon came to know that some of the letters were alike and some were not alike. She "saw" through feeling that the letters on the labels of two different things were themselves different. They were just as different as the real knife and the real fork.

After a few lessons Laura began to understand. The label for KNIFE somehow belonged to the knife. It was not part of the knife, but it meant the same thing. The label on the fork meant the same thing as the fork itself.

Soon Laura could find the right label to go with anything she could feel. When she was handed a knife, she could find the label KNIFE. Or, handed the word FORK, she would get a fork. Laura showed that she understood by taking the word CHAIR and placing it on the chair. The smile on her face showed how happy she was.

Slowly at first, and then with bursts of light in her mind, she began to learn for herself. She could know a thing by the feel of the label that went with it.

Little by little she began to understand that these words were made up of parts, or letters. Soon she could put letters together to make words. Before long she could "read" through her sense of touch. Now she could read words and sentences.

Because she knew the shapes of the letters, Laura was able to make those shapes herself. With a special board with raised marks, she could write.

97

Laura, who could not see or hear or talk, grew up to be a happy woman. She had found that she could learn many, many things through her sense of touch. She had the help of people who loved her. After years of hard work, Laura Bridgman had found a way to be a part of the world around her.

Christopher the CONTRARY CHAMELEON

Young Christopher Chameleon
  was very, very small;
A scant three inches, nose to tail,
  and less than one inch tall.
Now all chameleon children
  who do as they are told,
Must learn to match their background,
  and are never, never bold.
But Christopher Chameleon
  in a most contrary way,
Refused to change his color
  and just stayed pink all day.

"It makes me tired," said Christopher,
  "to change and change and change.
My head starts getting dizzy,
  and my stomach feels quite strange."
His parents scowled and scolded.
  They said, "This will not do.
You've got to match your background,
  no matter what the hue."
But Christopher Chameleon
  just yawned and said, "I think
I'll take a nap on this green leaf,"
  and stayed the same bright pink.

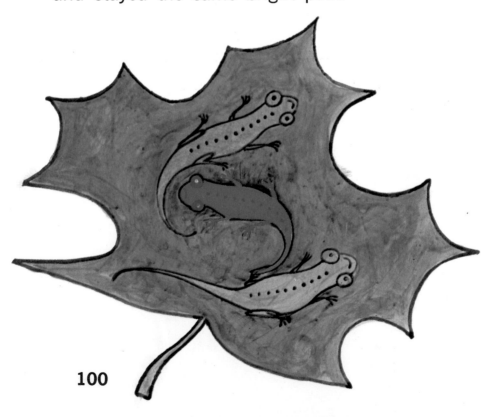

The rest of the chameleons
   matched places where they lay.
But drowsing little Christopher
   stood out as plain as day.
And so, a big crow sitting
   on a nearby maple tree
Saw something bright upon a leaf
   and swooped down close to see.
Christopher felt a shadow
   blocking out the sun
And opened one bright eye and knew
   the time had come to run !
Beneath the leaf he darted,
   as fast as he could go,
And then he clung there hoping
   that he had lost the crow.

101

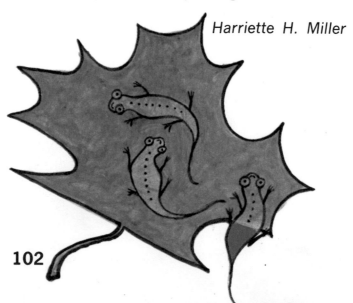

"I'm sure I spotted something,"
   croaked the crow from quite nearby.
"It looked like a pink lizard
   from up there in the sky."
"That crow saw me," thought Christopher,
   "from way up in the air.
He did not see the others,
   but he knew that I was there."
The crow flapped off, and Christopher
   peeked out, and when he'd seen
That it was safe, climbed on his leaf
   and quickly turned quite green.

Harriette H. Miller

Mr. Blynn's Crazy Kite

Andy and his friends were playing ball on the Campbells' farm. It was almost too windy to play ball. The sun was already setting. It was bright, bright red.

Andy was catching a ball. Up it sailed high into the air, and down it came into his mitt.

"Wow!" Andy Campbell and Ed Miller shouted.

Mrs. Campbell was watching from the back porch of the house. "You have far-seeing eyes, Andy," she said.

It was true. Andy's far-seeing eyes could find beetles touring around a meadow. He could see small birds hiding in the leaves of a tree. And when Mr. Blynn's kites sailed high in the air, Andy could track them touring across the sky.

Mr. Blynn was a farmer. When he finished his farm work, he made kites in a small workshop in an open meadow.

Some of the kites were five feet long. They had strange shapes. One was a big flat owl. One was curved at both ends.

Andy's favorite kite looked like a huge arrowhead. One end was pointed. The other end looked like a pair of wings.

It was fun watching Mr. Blynn fly his kites. Sometimes they dipped and crashed. Sometimes they flew out of sight. A few of them broke loose. Andy's far-seeing eyes helped Mr. Blynn track them across the sky.

Those far-seeing eyes helped Andy to catch balls pretty well too.

Mrs. Campbell called, "Do your best now, Andy. Time for one more throw. It's already suppertime." Then she went into the house.

"Throw the ball as high as you can," Bobby Brown yelled. "We'll try to catch it."

The ball soared into the air. Andy watched it go. Suddenly a strange object appeared in the sky. It glowed with reddish light.

What a queer thing it was! It looked like a saucer with a cup upside down on it.

Andy forgot about catching the ball. He stared and stared at the strange object. The other boys were staring at it too.

Bobby said, "Say, is that thing a flying saucer?" He ran across fields trying to keep up with the strange moving object.

Mrs. Campbell called, "What's going on?"

Ed Miller jumped up and down. He pointed at the object. "Call the police, Mrs. Campbell. There's a flying saucer!"

Andy's far-seeing eyes were already tracking the reddish glow. "Mr. Blynn will want to see this," he decided.

So Andy hopped on his bike and headed for Mr. Blynn's meadow.

Mr. Blynn was standing in the meadow and staring up at the strange object. In one hand he held some loose twine, and he was laughing to himself.

"Well, boy," Mr. Blynn said to Andy, "what do you think that is up there?"

"Is it a flying saucer?" Andy wondered. "With a cabin on top? It looks like one, all reddish and moving so fast."

"Wind's moving fast too," Mr. Blynn answered. "Did you notice that?"

"I forgot about the wind," Andy said.

"There's enough wind to give a kite a good lift of air," Mr. Blynn said. "A good lift of air is what makes it fun to fly a kite. I like to see what happens then."

Andy said slowly, "But that thing doesn't look like a kite, does it? What's that reddish light in the top part of it?"

The strange object was moving farther and farther away from them.

"Take one last look," Mr. Blynn suggested.

Andy squinted. "Maybe that is your kite, sir. I can see the pointed end and the wings. But what about that thing on top?"

Mr. Blynn smiled. "Maybe my kite and a weather balloon got mixed up with each other. Maybe they tangled. I guess a small instrument on the balloon tangled with my kite string and the kite broke loose."

Mr. Blynn let the loose string hang from his hand. He said, "Yes, sir, the kite broke loose, and the wind is carrying those two along together. That's my guess."

Andy had another question. "But how about that reddish light?"

Mr. Blynn winked. "Did you notice how red the sun was when it was setting?"

"Yes, sir. I noticed it when I was catching a ball over at the Campbells' farm."

"Well," Mr. Blynn said, "I guess the balloon-kite was up high too. High enough to catch some of the sun's reddish light."

Mr. Blynn looked at Andy and winked again. "That's your flying saucer, boy."

They both laughed.

"Yes, sir, Mr. Blynn, I guess it is. I'll go and tell the boys." And off went Andy to tell the news.

The Firefly

A Song

A little light is going by,
Is going up to see the sky,
A little light with wings.

I never could have thought of it,
To have a little bug all lit
And made to go on wings.

Elizabeth Madox Roberts

SPECIAL VISITORS

One summer Jeff and his family went to Colorado. Their cabin was high in the Rocky Mountains. It was near big woods, where hummingbirds live in the trees.

"They are so tiny and they fly so fast," Jeff said to his father. "How can I ever see what they look like?"

"We can set up a feeder for the hummingbirds," his father said. "We will set it up here at the cabin. Then some tiny hummers will surely come."

That summer Jeff often watched the hummingbirds. Day after day they came to sip the sweet red liquid in the feeder.

One day a beautiful male broad-tail came to the feeder. It sipped the sweet red liquid and was gone with a flash of its whirring wings. Then something like a tiny green helicopter moved through the air. A plain buffy-breasted hummer was coming to taste the red food. The flashy male whirred down and chased the buffy-breasted hummer into the woods. Back he came with a noisy whirr and perched on a limb of the tree.

Over and over that bossy male broad-tail chased away the other birds. Finally one hummingbird led the male far away through the trees. Other hummingbirds came and fed, until the bossy male chased them off.

"Where do they go in the woods?" Jeff wondered. "I wish I could find their nests."

Jeff had seen pictures of hummingbirds' nests in books. But he did want to see a real nest. He knew they were very small. He knew they were hard to find in the woods.

Day after day Jeff tracked a special path through the woods. He followed the birds when they left the feeder. He followed their flashing colors among the trees. He listened for their whirring wings. But summer was going fast, and he was still looking for a hummingbird's nest.

One chilly morning Jeff left the cabin after breakfast. He had on his red shirt. Hummingbirds like the color red. They often come near it, as they did to the feeder.

Jeff walked along his special path. He heard the hummers. Whirring wings came near. A tiny hummingbird was coming toward Jeff's red shirt. The bird dipped once. The whirring sound stopped. Jeff felt a fairy-like touch on his arm.

Then the buffy-breasted green hummer flew off to feed on some red flowers.

Jeff waited. When the tiny bird flew off into the woods, he tried to follow. He pushed through low branches of the trees. The nest must be near! But he could not find it.

He turned to leave the woods, and there was the nest close enough to touch. It was only as big as a nut shell. It looked like the other knots on the tree branch. But this knot was a nest. A hummingbird was in it.

Jeff walked around the nest. The small buffy-breasted mother's eyes followed him. She made little frightened fluttery sounds. Jeff stepped still closer. Away she flew. He tiptoed up and peeked down into the nest. He saw two very tiny eggs. They looked like small white beans.

Jeff reached out to touch them. He stopped, jamming his hands into his pockets. "No!" he said to himself, "I won't touch them."

He turned away from the nest. Very, very slowly, Jeff walked home.

He was late for lunch. His mother asked, "Where have you been all morning, Jeff?"

"Oh, in the woods. Dad, how long does it take for a baby hummingbird to fly?"

"Quite a while, Jeff."

"Can babies eat out of our feeder?"

"Yes, if they have a wire to perch on."

"Dad, will you help me put a wire perch on our feeder?"

"Sure, Jeff." With a smile his father asked, "Are you waiting for special visitors?"

"I just want to be ready," Jeff answered.

He helped his father bend a wire around the feeding tube. He kept the feeder filled. Hummingbirds came and went from the feeder. For quite a while every day, Jeff watched them sip the sweet colored liquid.

"How about those special visitors?" his Dad asked. "It's about time for them to come, isn't it?"

"Maybe," Jeff said. It was hard to wait and to keep on watching. But he did do it.

119

One morning a mother hummer and two baby hummers did come to the feeder. Jeff watched the babies with their short bills. One at a time the tiny hummers perched on the wire. They sipped the sweet red liquid.

Then they followed the mother bird into the woods. Jeff watched them go.

"Gee, I'm glad you hatched!" he called.

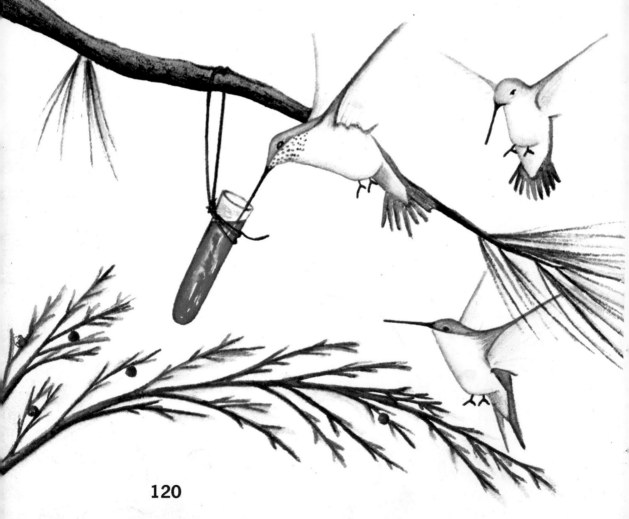

THE ADVENTURES OF MICHAEL McGEE

Michael McGee climbed up a tall tree,
And he said, "Golly gee!
  What things I can see!
From this tree in my yard
  I can look all around
And see sights you could never see
  down on the ground!
Look there, to the east,
  at that long, winding road.
No one knows that it leads
  to a dragon's abode.
I was there just today.
  I dropped in for a visit.
I knocked on the door, and he called out,
  'Who is it?'
'Well,' I answered, 'It's Mike,'
  and he said, 'Come on in.
I've been hoping you'd come.
  Say, old friend, how've you been?'

I helped him clean house
    and we washed all the dishes,
Then I played with the dragon—
    his name's Aloysius.
We played Chinese checkers
    and then went outside
Where I climbed on his back
    and he gave me a ride.
He gallops so fast
    that I have to hold tight
To the scales on his neck.
    We must be a sight
As we leap across rivers
    and climb over hills.
You just can't beat riding
    a dragon for thrills."

Then Mike's brother, Joe,
    rode his bike through the gate,
And he called out, "Hey, Mike!
    Hurry up! We'll be late!
What are you looking at? Why do you stare?
There's just that old road
    to the dump over there."
"Just a road to the dump? Maybe so,"
    answered Mike.
"From down where you are
    maybe that's what it's like.
But when I climb my tree,"
    said Michael McGee,
"The things I can see
    are as strange as can be."

Harriette Hunt Miller

123

Talking without Words

Laura Bridgman could make some sounds. But she could not talk. Because she could not talk, she used simple signs. Think of Laura when you do the exercises below.

1. What is the difference between making sounds and talking?
   Do you ever make sounds with your mouth without words? When and how?

2. Show you are surprised without using words. Now show these feelings without using words.

   afraid   cold   happy   hot
   angry   sleepy   hurt   sad

3. Suppose a new boy or girl in your classroom cannot speak English. How would you talk to him or her? How would he or she answer?
   Try these questions. How would you answer these questions without using words?

   How old are you?
   What is your name?
   Have you a dog?
   What game do you like to play?

4. Blindfold a friend and hand him or her an object. Let the friend feel the shape, size, and weight and guess what the object is. Use such objects as a pencil, orange, feather, eraser, and twig. Find other objects and play the game with another friend.

A Kite Puzzle

Read the first clue to the puzzle and find the answer in the lists below. Count the number of blanks for the first clue on the kite and be sure that your answer has the same number of letters. Do the rest in the same way. Write your answers on a piece of paper.

1. A place to fly a kite
2. People and animals drink this
3. What you hold to fly a kite
4. Something that flies straight up and down
5. To feel with the fingers
6. Words in order
7. It means only one
8. Where kites fly

liquid   meadow   visitors
object   single   reddish
field   sky   buffy-breasted
string   twine   sentences
touch   hummingbird

126

Animals Are Fun Too

127

To Rita from Gus

Rita lived near the seashore of Puerto Rico.[1] She often went sailing with her brother. Sometimes she sailed by herself.

One day, when the water was smooth, she went sailing alone. She stayed near the shore. The boat moved so slowly that she lay down and let it drift. She was almost asleep when a strong wind came up. The boat overturned.

[1] Puerto Rico (PWEHR·toh REE·koh)

When Rita woke up, she was in a cave. Then, to her surprise, something touched her arm. It was an octopus.

"Don't be afraid, Rita. I will not hurt you," he said. "You are in an underground cave. Come, let me show you around. Over there is the opening to the ocean from which I pulled you.

"In here," he said, pointing to another opening, "is an easy way to the ocean. Come on, let's go."

"I want to go home!" cried Rita.

The octopus shook his head. "I cannot let you do that. You see, you are here to take the place of Mr. Tuna's brother. Your father got him when he was fishing last week. Here! Take this seaweed. Keep tight hold of it and you can breathe under water."

He pushed her gently into the ocean. Having the magic seaweed, Rita could breathe under water. Soon she was quite at ease.

"We have electric lights down here," the octopus said very proudly. "Do you see them? Much better, we think.

"We now have new ways to get around. We have done away with the old clam-shell carriages. They were drawn by sea-horses and had round stones for wheels. We made the speedmobile. There's one now!" he cried, as a strange-looking thing whizzed past.

Just then a big fish came up. He stared at Rita for a while. Then he asked, "Caught an earthling, Gus?" Gus was the octopus's name.

"Yes," Gus said. "I'm showing her around."

130

Until then, Rita had not seen many fish. Now they were all around.

"Please, let me go home," she pleaded.

The octopus called Mr. Tuna to ask if he would let Rita go free. The answer was a loud "No!"

"What was that thing you used to call Mr. Tuna?" Rita asked.

"Oh, that's a shellaphone," was the answer. "It was made by Jack Eel."

In the days that followed, Rita and Gus became good friends. One day, after a turtle-egg breakfast, a watercress-sandwich lunch, and a reed and seaweed dinner, Gus drew Rita aside. He said in a whisper,

"I'll show you the way out now. Hurry, before you are seen."

He led her to the cave under the waterfall. At the end of the cave was a small tunnel. It was big enough for her to go through if she stooped. "Follow the tunnel. You'll come out on the beach near your house," he told her.

"Good-by, Gus," said Rita.

Gus placed a small box in her hand. Then he went away.

Rita awoke to find herself on the beach. Her adventure must have only been a dream. But what was this box in her hand?

Inside was a small shining shell. On the shell were these words:

To Rita from Gus

What really happened, Rita wondered.

Bears Aren't Everywhere[1]

One night Danny's mother read him a book about bears. The book was about brown bears and black bears, cinnamon bears and a polar bear.

Then Danny's mother put out the light and said, "Good night, sleep tight, Danny."

But Danny did not sleep tight.

Danny lay in bed and thought about bears.

133

All of a sudden bears were everywhere—brown bears, black bears, cinnamon bears. And a polar bear was at the window.

Danny put his head under the covers, and the bears went away.

The next morning Danny forgot all about the bears. He helped his father feed the chickens and bring in the eggs from the nests. Then Danny went exploring.

He climbed the hill behind the farmhouse. He stood high on the hill and looked down on the farm below. The cold wind blew in his face.

Danny saw that everything was changing. The goldenrod had changed from gold to golden brown. The leaves on some of the trees were changing from green to orange, red, and yellow.

Then Danny ran down the hill to the orchard. He saw that the apples were changing too. They were turning from sour green to red and yellow.

Danny did some exploring. He looked into the hole where a woodchuck lived. But the woodchuck wasn't at home.

"I think the woodchuck must be out eating someplace," said Danny to himself. "He wants to get as fat as he can, so that he can have a good sleep in the winter."

Danny climbed over the old stone wall, but just as he got to the edge of the woods, he heard a noise.

What kind of a noise was that—or was it a noise at all?

It wasn't a bong or a bang.

It was more of a crackle or crunch.

Danny thought about bears—brown bears, black bears, cinnamon bears, and the polar bear he had seen at his window.

Danny turned around.

He walked as quietly as he could walk, over the old stone wall, through the orchard.

Then he ran. Danny ran as fast as he could run.

"There's a bear down there," yelled Danny to his mother, as he slammed the kitchen door.

When Danny's father came in from milking the cows that night, Danny said, "There's a bear down there."

"Where, down there?" asked Danny's father.

"Down below the orchard in the woods," Danny answered.

"Then you and I will go down to the woods in the morning and find him," Danny's father said.

But Danny didn't want to go down to the woods with his father. He didn't want to go exploring and find the bear.

When Danny went to bed that night, the bears were everywhere—brown bears, black bears, cinnamon bears, and the polar bear at the window.

"What kind of a bear is waiting in the woods down there?" said Danny to himself.

Then he put his head under the covers, and the bears all went away.

When Danny woke up in the morning, he couldn't see a thing. The fields, the trees, the barn—all the world around his house was covered with a soft white fog.

No wind was blowing. Everything was still.

"Come on, Danny," Danny's father said after breakfast. "We're going down to find the bear."

"Not this morning," Danny said. "I have to feed the chickens and bring in the eggs."

"Oh, no," Danny's father said. "I need you, Danny. I need you to show me where the bear is hiding in the woods."

So Danny had to go with his father to the woods to find the bear.

Danny and his father walked down the hill together. They walked in the still white fog.

"Like ghosts," said Danny.

His father said, "Put your feet down carefully. Don't make any noise."

When they came to the orchard, Danny and his father stood still and listened.

And sure enough !

Danny heard the noise again.

It wasn't a bong or a bang.

It was more of a crackle and crunch.

"There's the bear," Danny said very softly.

A soft wind blew.

The white fog swirled around.

Danny and his father stood very still and listened.

Danny didn't want to go exploring over the old stone wall and into the woods. Danny just wanted to run home as fast as he could run. He wanted to slam the kitchen door.

But Danny's father took his hand, and they went over the wall and into the woods together.

There was the noise again.

Not a bong or a bang, but a crackle and crunch, in the dry leaves scattered on the ground.

Danny stopped and looked and listened.

Just then a fat gray squirrel ran up the trunk of a great big walnut tree. When the squirrel leaped from branch to branch to branch, he shook walnuts down. They fell with a crunch and crackle into the dry leaves scattered on the ground.

Danny laughed and so did his father.

"Some bear," Danny said.

His father smiled. "I guess bears aren't really everywhere, are they, Danny?"

"I guess not," Danny said.

"And don't you think," said Danny's father, "that it would be better to be SURE it's a bear, before you get so frightened of a bear that's not even there?"

Danny knew that his father was right.

"My bear was just a fat gray squirrel getting ready for winter," Danny said.

"That's a good idea," said his father.

So Danny and his father filled their pockets full of walnuts and took them home to dry.

A long time after that Danny sat beside the fire and cracked his walnuts, while the wind blew against the window and the snow was deep outside.

"I wonder," Danny said, "if underneath the snow someplace, or in some hollow tree—"

"A big brown bear is waiting for you?" Danny's father said.

"No," laughed Danny, "but I wonder if underneath the snow someplace, or in some hollow tree, that fat gray squirrel is eating walnuts just like me?"

A PET NAMED JET

One morning when Judy came to her new school on Pepper Street, the children were chasing a stray cat. It was black and thin, and Judy felt sorry for it. A boy named Ross caught the cat and lifted it by the back of the neck. It hung like dirty worn-out fur.

"It's an old tomcat," Ross said. "Let's wash him off." He started for the drinking fountain.

"Stop it!" Judy cried. She put her lunch down, ran after Ross, and pulled at his arm. The cat jumped free and began to run.

143

Ross was angry. All at once he said, "Black cats are bad luck! Don't let him cross your path!"

The children ran, and Judy was glad when the cat got away.

At lunch time, as Judy started to look for her lunch, she heard some children laughing. Then she saw Ross hiding her sandwich. When she ran at him, he acted afraid.

"Don't cross my path!" he shouted.

The other children ran away when Judy came near, and Judy felt angry. She wanted her sandwich! Just then a teacher came out.

"What's going on?" she asked.

"Nothing, Miss Downs," the children said.

"Nothing, Miss Downs," said Judy, trying not to cry.

Miss Downs looked upset. Judy liked Miss Downs.

But Judy said to herself, "The children at this school don't like me. Miss Downs can't change that!"

"Come inside, Judy," Miss Downs said softly.

As they went in, Kim handed Judy a paper bag. "I hope you'll like what's in the bag, Judy," she said, trying to be friendly.

All Judy wanted was to be back at her old school, with her old friends.

After school Judy took a short cut home through an alley. She saw the same cat lying in the dirt. He was thin and scrawny. His eyes were big and gold. Judy tried to pet him, but the big scrawny tomcat stayed out of reach. When she started on, he followed her along the alley.

Judy coaxed him into her house with some scraps of meat. The cat ate them and yowled for more.

"My, my!" said Judy's mother. "That cat hasn't had anything to eat for days!"

Judy gave him a saucer of milk. "May I keep him, Mama?" she asked, pouring more milk into the saucer.

In her mind Judy saw him fat and glossy.

Her father laughed. "You can try," he said. "But that old tomcat may have something to say about anybody keeping him."

Judy bent over and patted the cat. "I'll call him Jet," she said, "like the buttons on Mama's black coat."

After dinner she tried to pet him, but Jet jumped down. The scrawny old tomcat curled up at her feet, tucking his tail under himself. Oh, how Judy wanted Jet to be her pet.

"That is one proud cat," said her father. "You'll never make a lap-cat out of him."

146

Every day after that Jet met Judy in the alley. Every day she fed and brushed him. His coat grew silky. His bones no longer showed. Still he would not lie on her lap.

Judy said to herself, "Jet is my friend just the same."

At school Ross still teased her, and Judy still chased him. Sometimes Ross would hide her lunch, and someone would laugh. That made Judy angry.

One day Judy found Jet sitting on the alley fence. The sun shone on his fur and his eyes were slits of gold. As Judy came up, a man shouted, "Scat, cat!" He threw some water at Jet.

Judy ran to pick him up, but Jet darted away. A man called over the fence, "If that's your cat, keep him out of my yard."

Judy looked up and down the alley for Jet. Then she walked along calling, "Jet! Jet!" The cat was gone. Judy cried as she walked home. Would she ever see Jet again?

When she reached home, there lay Jet, stretched out by the kitchen stove, washing himself.

"He's been home quite a while," said her mother. "He was sopping wet."

Judy picked Jet up and hugged him. "Poor Jet!" she said.

She brushed him before dinner. After dinner she brushed him some more. When his fur shone again, she put down the brush.

"Now," she said, "he'll let me pet him."

But the cat jumped down, stretched, then curled up at her feet as he always did. Judy sighed, "Is he really my friend, Papa?"

Her father laughed. "He is your friend. He's just too proud to sit in your lap."

Judy wondered about that word. "What is 'proud'?" she asked.

" 'Proud' to that cat," said her father, "means he doesn't care what other people think about him."

Judy's eyes filled. "But I love him," she said.

"And he loves you. But if you didn't love him," said her father, "that old cat wouldn't cry about it. Because he likes himself just the way he is. He says, 'I'm Jet. You can take me or leave me.'"

Judy thought about being proud. She wished she could be like Jet. She would say, "Take me or leave me. I'm Judy."

Then she thought, "I am Judy! I will be proud, like Jet."

The next morning she made two lunches. At school she left one on a bench and hid the other in her coat. Kim and another girl were playing hop-scotch near the bench.

"May I play too?" Judy asked.

Kim said, "All right." The other girl walked off. Judy was hurt, but this time she did not cry or get angry.

"I'm Judy," she thought. "You can take me or leave me."

Kim smiled and said, "You can be first."

As they played, there was an angry shout, and then they heard boys laughing. Judy looked. Ross had her lunch again. This time he bit into the sandwich, made a face, and spit out the food.

"What's wrong with Ross?" Kim asked.

Judy laughed. "Maybe he doesn't like the soap flakes I put in my sandwich today."

151

Miss Downs came out. "What's going on?" she called.

"Nothing," Ross sputtered. He didn't look at Judy.

"Nothing, Miss Downs," said the other children, laughing.

"Well, come inside," Miss Downs said. "Judy, I'm glad to see you have a lunch today."

Miss Downs was smiling at Judy, as if she were thinking, "You're Judy—and I'll take you."

THE INVITATION

Nancy Ann walked down the country road. She was on her way home from school. In her hand was a picture of the schoolhouse, cut out of red paper. On it was written: "Come to the fair! At Lone Oak School, Saturday at 2 o'clock."

Michael caught up with her. He and Nancy Ann were both in the same grade. They lived near each other, and they often walked home together.

153

He saw what was in her hand. "Is that an invitation to our fair?" he asked.

"Yes," she said.

"What are you going to do with it?" he asked.

"I know what I'd *like* to do with it," she said. "I'd like to throw it away."

He looked surprised. "Why?" he asked.

"Because it's for Mrs. Peacham, that's why," said Nancy Ann. "The teacher says we should invite her because she's new here. I go past her house on the way home, so I have to give her this invitation and tell her about the fair!" Nancy Ann made a face.

"Don't you like her?" asked Michael.

"No, I don't," said Nancy Ann.

"But you don't even know her, do you?" asked Michael.

"I know her well enough," said Nancy Ann. "I went past her farm last month, and I thought I saw a pony. I went closer, and it *was* a pony, tied under an apple tree. I was going to pet him, and just then old Mrs. Peacham came running out of the house. She waved her arms and said, 'Stop. Don't take any of those apples!'"

"You weren't going to, were you?" asked Michael.

"Of course I wasn't," said Nancy Ann. "I told her I wasn't, and then I ran home."

"And now you have to go back," said Michael.

"Yes," said Nancy Ann. "I don't see why the teacher couldn't have asked someone else."

They came to Mrs. Peacham's farm. It was a small farm, with a house almost hidden by trees. A lane led to the house.

Michael waited while Nancy Ann went down the lane. The house was quiet. She stood on the porch for a little while, but she did not knock. She put the invitation down in front of the door. Then she tiptoed away.

She went back to the road. "There!" she said. "I left the invitation."

"Wasn't she at home?" asked Michael.

"I don't know," said Nancy Ann.

Come to the fair!

"I thought you were supposed to *give* her the invitation," said Michael. "I thought you were supposed to tell her about the fair."

"I was," said Nancy Ann, "but I didn't want her to come out and shout at me."

They walked down the road. Michael asked, "Did you promise the teacher to stop and tell Mrs. Peacham about the fair?"

Nancy Ann began to walk more slowly. "I did promise," she said. "I'd better go back."

"I'll go back with you," said Michael.

They went back to Mrs. Peacham's. They walked down the lane. The invitation was where Nancy Ann had left it. She picked it up and knocked at the door. Michael stood beside her.

A little old woman opened the door. She put her head on one side like a bird, and looked at them.

"I brought you this, Mrs. Peacham," said Nancy Ann. She held out the invitation.

Mrs. Peacham took it. "I can't read it without my glasses," she said.

"It's an invitation—to our fair at school," said Nancy Ann. "We're going to have an art show—and songs—and games."

"Didn't you come to see me one day?" asked Mrs. Peacham. "Didn't you run away before I could talk to you?"

"I—I didn't think you wanted me here," said Nancy Ann. "You thought I was taking your apples—and I wasn't. All I wanted was to see the pony."

"You didn't take any apples?" said Mrs. Peacham. "That's good, because they were green. I was afraid you might take a bite of a green apple and have a stomach-ache. There's nothing worse than a green-apple stomach-ache. But the apples are ripe now. Why don't you two go and pick some?"

"Thank you, we will," said Michael.

159

They went around the house to the apple tree. The branches were hanging down with big red apples. And under the tree was the pony. His sides were fat. His brown coat shone in the sunlight.

"Oh, he's beautiful!" said Nancy Ann.

"His name is Sam," said Mrs. Peacham. "Would you like to ride him?"

"Could we?" asked Nancy Ann.

"Yes," said Mrs. Peacham. "Just climb on. Sam will know what to do."

Michael helped Nancy Ann up on the pony's back. The pony trotted around the apple tree. He ran in two neat circles before he stopped.

Then Michael took his turn.

"I used to keep ponies in the city," said Mrs. Peacham. "I used to run a pony ride in the park for boys and girls. But my rheumatism got worse. I couldn't help the boys and girls off and on any more, so I sold my ponies, all but Sam. He was my favorite. When I came to the country to live, I just had to bring him with me."

"I'm sorry about your rheumatism," said Nancy Ann. "Will you be well enough to come to the fair?"

"I'm much better in the country," said Mrs. Peacham. "If I do come to the fair, could Sam come? I think he misses the boys and girls. Besides, he needs exercise. You and your friends could have free rides."

"That would really be wonderful!" said Nancy Ann.

"Ask your teacher how she likes the idea," said Mrs. Peacham, "and let me know what she says."

"Our teacher will like it," said Michael. "She couldn't help liking it."

"Now," said Mrs. Peacham, "why don't we pick some apples?"

So they picked apples and sat under the tree to eat them.

"It's like a picnic," said Nancy Ann. "Here, Sam, come to the picnic."

And the pony came straight to where they were sitting and joined the picnic, and ate an apple too.

The Tutor

A tutor who tooted a flute,
Tried to teach two young tooters to toot.
Said the two to the tutor,
"Is it harder to toot, or
To tutor two tooters to toot?"

Carolyn Wells

163

Reading a Picture Story

A rebus story uses pictures instead of words. In the story below you will need to use each pair of pictures to make one word. See if you can read this funny story.

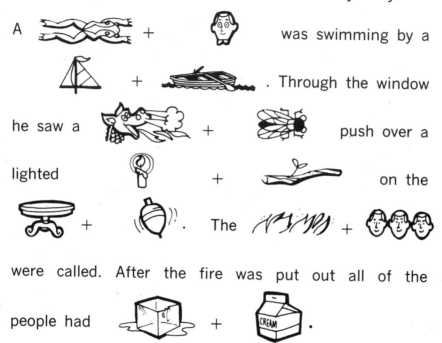

were called. After the fire was put out all of the people had

What is a compound word? How many compound words are there in this story?

Write a rebus story of your own. Here are some words that may help you: _stoplight_, _horseshoe_, _tablespoon_, _catfish_, _kneecap_. You may think of others. Did you find that your rebus story took longer to write than other stories? Would you like to use rebus writing all of the time? Why or why not?

Make Up a Name

When a new machine is made, a new name has to be thought of for it. *Shellaphone* was a new machine made by Jack Eel. You can tell where the name *Speedmobile* came from. Look at the picture below.

What is happening in the picture? What is a good name for this machine?

What is a good name for a machine that spreads jam on bread?

What name would you give a machine that can cut and paste at the same time?

What is a good name for a machine that picks up apples and puts them in boxes?

Draw a picture of a new machine and think of a name for it.

166

The World
Around Us

167

GUESS AND TRY

Mom poured her coffee, piping hot, and she left it on the breakfast table. Mom often poured her coffee this way.

I drank my milk and ate my breakfast, but Mom's coffee stayed in the cup. She was fixing lunches for Dad and me. We were in a hurry.

My dad is a teacher. He teaches science, and sometimes we talk things over. But he won't answer some of my questions about science. He always says, "Guess and try."

Mom was a long time fixing the lunches. Dad grabbed his, and rushed off to teach his science class. Mom tasted her coffee and made a funny face.

"Too cold," she said. She threw it away and poured some hot coffee into her cup.

I picked up my lunch and walked to school. I had time to think, so I said to myself, "How come Mom's coffee got cold?"

But I didn't have time to guess and try to find out why hot coffee in a cup cooled off.

We eat our lunches out of doors at our school. Sometimes it gets hot out there. Sometimes Pedro Juarez sits near me. This day he did.

He likes milk. I do too. We buy cartons of milk for lunch at school. I like my milk good and cold. So I drink it right away.

Pedro pours his milk into a saucer, which he brings in his lunch pail every day. The milk sits in the saucer while Pedro eats. "I let my milk warm up," he always says.

Here was a funny thing! My mom poured hot coffee into a cup, and it cooled off. Pedro pours cold milk into a saucer, and it warms up. "What's going on around here?" I say to myself. "Has this anything to do with science?"

I talked to my dad about it after school.

"What's going on with the coffee and the milk?" I asked. "Anything to do with science?"

My dad winked. "Guess and try," he said.

So I did. Mom helped me pour some hot coffee into a cup. I poured some ice-cold milk into a saucer, myself. And then I waited.

I worked with Tricks, my Scotty dog. She goes to Obedience School and is learning to sit when I say, "Sit." It is hard work.

"How about that coffee and milk?" Dad called.

So I tried to find out. I put my finger into the coffee. It was not too hot, but it was not really cold.

I put my finger into the milk and swished it around in the saucer. I made small waves.

"How about it?" Dad called again.

"Oh," I said. "Funny thing. The milk isn't so cold now and the coffee isn't very hot. Each one is sort of cool."

My dad laughed. "Sort of ?" he called.

"Well, the milk is cool," I called back. "The coffee feels warm, but it doesn't sting my finger."

Dad came out to look. He didn't try the coffee or the milk. He just said, "Maybe you have something here."

I wanted to be sure. So I dumped the coffee and the milk into the sink. Then I saw Dad looking at the cup and the saucer. It made me wonder. I looked at them too.

"Guess I'll try something new," I said.

"What ?" Dad asked.

"Guess what," I said. I didn't want to tell him. So Dad had to wait too.

I asked Mom for some more hot coffee, but I didn't use the cup. Saucers were more fun. I took two saucers this time. Mom poured the hot coffee into the other saucer.

"I am going to leave them here all night," I said.

Tricks went to bed and so did I. Sometimes Tricks sleeps in my room on her own blanket. This was one of those times. I always sleep harder when Tricks is snoring nearby. I guess she sleeps harder too.

We were the last ones up for breakfast.

Mom was making sandwiches. Dad was eating scrambled eggs. And my two saucers were sitting there on the kitchen table.

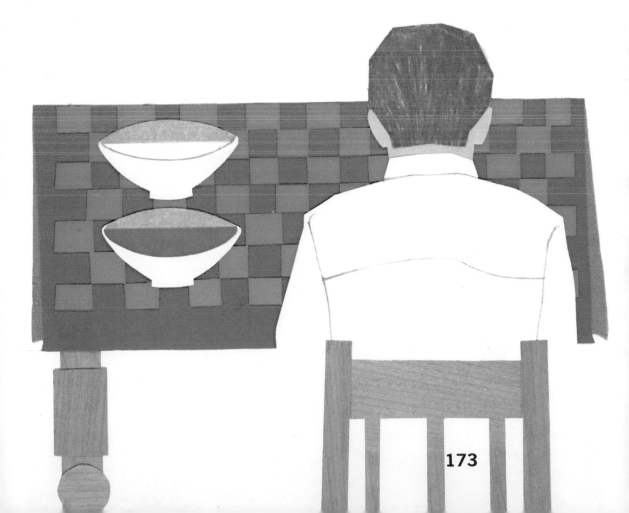

I put my finger into the milk and made small waves with it. It felt just right for swimming. I put a finger of my other hand into the saucer of coffee. At last I understood.

I looked at my Dad, and he was looking at me.

"It's something to do with science," I told him. "Guess and try."

And he said, "I did. That's how I know."

So now we two know the answer.

Do you?

DIPPY'S DAY
BY MOONLIGHT

It was evening on the desert. A full moon was rising. Dippy's day was just coming.

Desert sand in the daytime is too hot for a kangaroo rat like Dippy. He covers the openings of his house with dirt and sleeps in one room all day.

Night was daytime for Dippy. He woke up and stretched. He hopped around on his long hind legs to open the doors of his burrow.

That was easy! He just kicked aside little piles of dirt and let the moonlight come into the burrow.

175

Then he sat in a doorway on his hind legs and cleaned himself the way a cat does. He cleaned behind his ears. He smoothed his white front hairs and the tan fur on his back. He did not skip over his short front legs. When he finished, even the tuft of fur on his tail was fluffy and clean.

Breakfast came next. His little feet had made tiny tracks to nearby bushes. Dippy hopped off to them now. He sat up on his hind legs in front of some fat seeds and balanced himself with his long tail. With his front paws he brushed seeds from the stems into his open mouth.

A twig cracked close by! Dippy jumped ten feet. He changed his direction in midair. With zigzag leaps he reached the nearest hole into his burrow.

Inside he stopped, balanced himself, and trembled. His black eyes were wide open as he peeked out. A snake was going into the burrow of a neighbor rat, but Dippy was safe.

He stopped trembling and listened to other sounds. His ears spun around in different directions. Sand grains were blowing in the wind, and the full moon was higher. No snakes were near.

Dippy leaped to a spot of moonlight and froze again. Overhead an owl swished by, but it missed Dippy. Some other kangaroo rat might not be so lucky!

Dippy jumped to a clump of grasses. His front paws held some stems while his sharp teeth cut them off. He put them down to dry in a hollow of sand. He went from clump to clump, gathering his food and putting it to dry in the hollow.

It was hard work and his fur was full of dirt. He found a few seeds to eat, and then he headed for a bath in a dust hole.

It was just a hollow in the sand, but Dippy tested it well. There were tracks of birds and other animals all around it. There were some kangaroo-rat tracks too. This must be a favorite dust hole for a good bath.

Dippy hopped back to a nearby shadow. He looked and listened and waited. Nothing came to bother him, and into the dust hole he leaped.

He rolled around on his back in the hollow. He twisted and wiggled and turned. The dust was his bath water. It worked its way all through his fur and got rid of insects and twigs and dirt. It felt good!

Dippy finished his bath and jumped back to the shadow to brush himself. His white and tan fur was soon smooth again. The tuft on the end of his tail was fluffy.

A twig snapped, and Dippy zigzagged with big hops to get away from some new danger. Trembling, he waited until the desert was quiet, and looked around with his bright black eyes.

He saw kangaroo rats in the moonlight. They were playing tag and leapfrog on a sand hill, so he played with them.

All at once an owl hooted. Each rat leaped to his own burrow. A high scream told Dippy that one rat had not leaped fast enough.

A breeze carried the scent of ripe seeds to Dippy, and he was really hungry. He found some and ate a few. Then he filled his cheek pouches with some. His cheek pouches were fur-lined, a good basket for his seeds.

He carried them to a soft spot in the sand. He hid them in a little hollow and covered them. Back he went for more, always following the scent.

But another kangaroo rat was already stuffing his cheek pouches with seeds. Dippy leaped at him and landed, back to back, against the other rat. They kicked hard with their hind feet, and the sand flew in all directions. Each rat tried to keep his balance, but Dippy was bigger. One kick landed in the right spot. Over went the other rat. He rolled over and over, and Dippy chased him away.

Dippy went back to gather his seeds, but they were gone. Another rat had helped himself while Dippy was fighting.

His moonlight day was almost over, and he lost no time. He sat up on his hind legs and his nose twitched.

The right scent came, and he found more seeds. He ate some and then filled his cheek pouches. This time he took the seeds into his own burrow and stored them.

Daylight was coming. Dippy ate his supper and pushed dirt into each door of his burrow. He went into his sleeping room. He turned around and covered his nose with the fur tuft on his tail. One more wonderful day by moonlight was over, and it was bedtime for Dipodomys,[1] the little kangaroo rat of the desert.

[1] Dipodomys (digh·PO·də·mis)

182

The dark gray clouds,
the great gray clouds,
the black rolling clouds are elephants
going down to the sea for water.
They draw up the water in their trunks.
They march back again across the sky.
They spray the earth with the water,
and men say it is raining.

—from India

WHERE IS WATER?

Everyone knows the answer to that question. When rain falls, we see water in puddles. Sometimes water rushes down the side of a mountain, carrying rocks with it. In a quiet lake, water is like a mirror. You can see the sky reflected in it.

Water floats leaves and little sticks in a running river. Sometimes there is so much water that it floods the land. At the seashore great waves of water come in from the ocean. They rise in a tower of foam and fall back into the ocean again.

Sometimes water is not so easy to see. It is inside plants and animals. It is in all of us. Did you know that you are made mostly of water ?

Water is almost everywhere. It spreads out when we spill it. It soaks into things. It may be flowing into a lake at one spot and quietly flowing out at another. It fills low places.

Water is liquid. It can be clean enough to drink or it can be full of mud and dirt. It can also be salty, as it is in the ocean.

Water will not burn. It can help to put out fires.

Wonderful, wonderful water !

Yes, it is a liquid. But is it always a liquid ?

Doesn't running water change when cold, cold winter comes ? Is water always a liquid then ?

When it gets very cold, water has another form. It turns to ice. When ice is thick enough, you can run over it and skate on it.

Ice is water in its solid form. So is hail that pelts down in round, hard balls.

Glaciers and icebergs are water in this solid form. Have you ever seen a glacier ? Most glaciers are in high mountains. The ice in glaciers moves so slowly that you cannot see it move. But it does move. A mountain glacier is a solid river of snowy ice, that may move one inch in one day !

If the lower end of the glacier reaches the sea, great blocks of ice break off into the water. They are icebergs.

Snow is water in its solid form, because snow is made of delicate crystals of ice.

Where do snow crystals come from? And raindrops? And clouds? Where does the water they are made of come from? Do you ever wonder about that?

Here is one way to help you find out. Put a few drops of water in a saucer. Leave it there for a day or so. Then look at it again. The water is gone. It has gone into the air but you cannot see it there.

Lakes and oceans are like giant saucers that never dry up. So there must be lots of water in the air all the time.

Do you think this is where raindrops come from ? And snow ? And clouds ?

There is another way you may find out if water is really in the air. On a cold winter day, stand near a cold windowpane. Blow out a big breath of air against the glass. Do it again and again.

A foggy spot will come on the glass. Small drops of water will start to run down it. They were not there before you blew on the glass.

This form of water is in the air all the time. It was in your breath and you could not see it. Sneaky, isn't it ?

This is the third form of water. It is water vapor. Clouds and snow and raindrops all come from water vapor in the air.

Rain and snow and hail always fall. Rivers always run downhill. How does water get back up to make more rain and snow and hail ?

Do you ever wonder about that ?

189

SHADOWS ON THE MOON

What does the moon look like as it rides along in the sky? Do you ever play in the moonlight, and make shadows with your fingers? Do you ever play tag in the moonlight, and make shadows as you run?

Some people even find pictures in the moon and tell stories about them. Have you ever seen Moon-Boy in the moon? Some Indians in Alaska did. They were watching the moon, and they saw Moon-Boy. They were sure of it. They said that Moon-Boy spoke to the moon. They heard what he said. They told their children the story about it.

MOON-BOY[1]

At first, Moon-Boy lived on earth in a big family. He was a hunter. One day he came home late and hungry. But the food kettle was empty.

"There is nothing left to eat," his father said. When Moon-Boy began to cry, his father shouted, "Stop crying or I shall whip you!"

So the boy took the empty kettle and ran into the woods.

[1] Adapted from *The Moon Is a Crystal Ball* by Natalia Belting, copyright, 1952, by The Bobbs-Merrill Company, Inc., reprinted by permission of the publisher.

The night was clear. The moon was shining and full. Soon the Indians saw a strange shadow on the moon's face. Before that night it had always been clear, they said.

"It is the shadow of the boy," one Indian cried. "He is holding an empty kettle."

The boy was talking to the moon. They could hear his words.

"You, Moon," he said, "you are my father now. I will stay with you and have plenty to eat. My name is Sakesada. I am 'He-Who-Sits-On-The-Moon.'" And there he stayed.

He is very old now, the Indians say. He can no longer stand up straight. He is bent over halfway. You can see him there when the moon is shining and full.

MOON SHADOWS

Is Sakesada a shadow on the moon's face? Can you find a shadow there and tell a story about it?

It is fun to let your fingers dance and make shadows in the moonlight. It is fun to make up stories about the shadows on the moon.

The best fun is to find out why the moon has shadows, as it comes and goes in the sky.

Some day a spaceship may take you to the moon. You may really sit on it and take pictures of its mountains, or measure its big holes, called craters. Then you can zoom home to tell us what you found.

We do know some things to tell you before you go.

The moon is our nearest neighbor in space. It has flat places, high pointed mountains, and wide craters.

There is no air on the moon. There are no clouds, no wind, no rain. So there is no water. There are no rivers, no oceans.

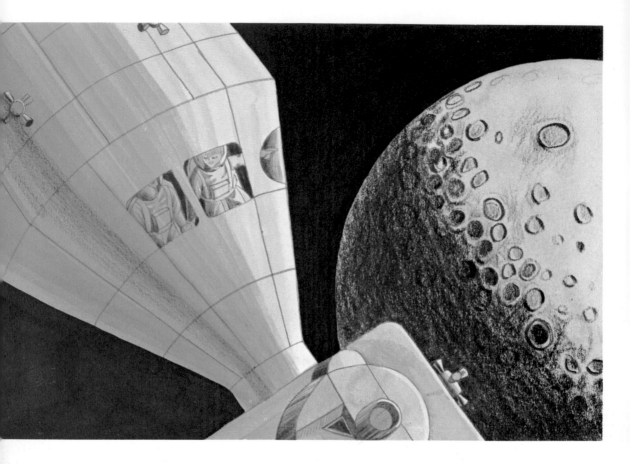

You will see stars in the daytime, if you go to the moon. They will be clear bright points of light, and the sky will be dark.

When we see the full moon rise in the sky, it glows with light. The moon looks like a shining silver ball, doesn't it? But the moon has no light of its own.

Where does the shining light on the moon's face come from? It comes from the sun and is reflected from the face of the moon.

Where there are mountains on the moon's face, the light makes shadows. They always point away from the sun.

Scientists look at pictures of the moon's shadows and measure them.

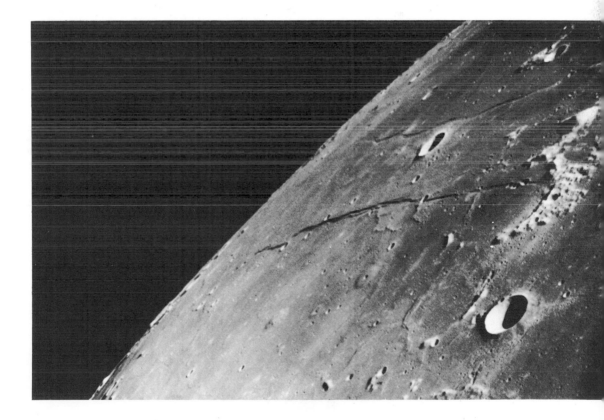

These scientists can measure how high the mountains are by their shadows. When the mountains are very high, the shadows are long and shaped like ice cream cones.

In these shadows the moon is colder than anything we know on the earth.

The pictures also show big craters on the moon. Scientists think that one of the craters may be 140 miles wide !

140 miles wide

Shadows tell us about the craters. They show that there are rings of mountains around these big holes. There are also mountains in the centers of some craters.

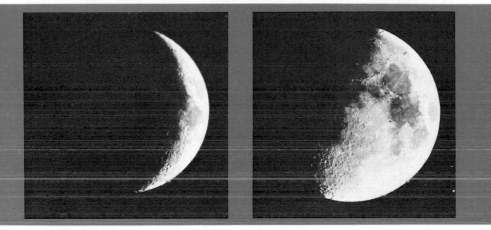

The moon shows us many "faces" as it rides along in the sky. It may be a thin crescent of light. It may look like a big letter D. The crescent, the letter D, and the full moon all reflect light from the sun.

Shadows have all kinds of stories to tell. There are old stories about Moon-Boy who lived on the moon. There are true stories which spacemen are telling nowadays. There will be new stories that you can tell *after* you take a trip to see the shadows on the moon.

THE EARTH OUR HOME

The Earth is our home. What sort of home it is depends on how we treat it, just as the houses we live in depend on how we take care of them.

Do you like to fish or swim? Do you like to walk or ride through the woods? Do you like to breathe fresh air? Or to watch birds and hear them sing?

If you do, we'll all have to treat our Earth home in a different way. Why?

198

Because we are making lakes and rivers too dirty for fish to live in or for boys and girls to swim in.

Because we're cutting down our forests too fast, we are spoiling the countryside.

Because we're making so much smoke, dirty air often hides the sky and even nearby things. The dirty air makes it hard for us to breathe, and it makes our eyes water.

Because we're putting so much poison on the things birds eat, they are finding it hard to live.

Because we throw away things we do not want or need, we litter our streets and highways.

There are many things we do to live, to keep warm, and to move about that spoil the earth, the air, and the water.

Have you seen smoke pouring out of tall factory chimneys? Have you smelled the gas fumes from the back of a bus? Have you noticed the smoke from a jet plane taking off? All of these things make the air dirty—they pollute it.

Have you seen dirty streams pouring from factories? Have you wondered where the sewage from one house, many houses, a big city goes? It pollutes rivers and lakes and may even make them die. Fish can't live in them, and you can't swim in them. Even the ocean is getting a little sick.

Have you wondered where the wood for houses comes from? And the paper for books and newspapers? From our forests. And what does the land look like when the trees are gone?

Have you thought where the poison goes that we spray on gardens and grass to kill insects and weeds? Onto the things the birds eat, making it hard for them to live and share with us their beautiful colors and songs.

Have you seen piles of old cars and old refrigerators? Not very nice to look at, are they? Have you seen piles of old boxes, glass jars, and cans? Not very beautiful, are they?

If we don't do anything about this spoiling of the world around us—its air, its water, its land, and its life—our lives are not going to be so nice. But there is much that we can do.

Factories can clean their smoke. Cars and planes can be made so that their fumes do not add to the pollution.

The dirty water from factories can be made clean. Sewage, too, can be changed so that water is clean enough to use again. Fish can live again, and you can swim again in oceans, rivers, and lakes.

The mountains can still be covered with forests if the cutting of trees is done with care. We must plant again where we have cut. And we can have enough wood for houses and paper for books.

Many of the things we use are worn out and cannot be used any more. But they do not have to be left around. We can change many things back into what they were made of, and use them again. Old newspapers can become new paper. Old glass jars can be turned into new glass. Old iron can help to make new cars and refrigerators.

We can also learn not to litter. We all know the sign: DO NOT LITTER. But not everyone does what the sign says.

For a long time, people have used their Earth home without thinking of what was happening to it. Now we see that we must treat it better if it is to be a nice home. It can be.

Solid, Liquid, or Vapor?

Which things in the picture are solid?
Which things are liquid?
Which things are vapor?

Science Experiments

1. Put a small pan of water in a sunny window. Put another small pan of water away from the sunshine. What happened to the water after two days? Which pan became empty first? Why?

2. Hang a wet towel in the classroom in the morning. In the late afternoon feel the towel. What happened? Where did the water go?

3. Remove the labels from two soup cans. Paint one can black and the other white. Put a thermometer in each can. Place them in a sunny window. Wait a few hours and check the temperature. Which can had the higher temperature? What have you learned about color and heat?

4. Place a plant on a windowsill in the sun. After two days look at the plant carefully. How has it changed? Which way did the plant lean? Now turn the plant around and check it again in two days. What happened? Why?

Once There Was

THE HANDRE

Once there was a handre. A handre is like a goblin, and this handre was very ugly. His great eyes rolled around. He had long sharp teeth and long sharp claws, which rattled. What he liked best was to jump out from behind a rock to frighten two certain little cats, who lived in a house down the road. He rolled his eyes, rattled his claws, and snarled at them. Then he vanished. The little cats would run home as fast as they could and hide in their beds.

One day the two little cats needed some butter and salt to put in their morning tea. "Let's go to the market," said one.

"What if we should meet the handre?" said the other.

They talked it over a while and decided that they would take a chance. "Maybe he has moved away," said one.

So off they went to market for butter and salt. On their way home, sure enough, out popped the handre from behind the rock, rolling his eyes. He rattled his claws and snarled.

Away they ran. But this time the handre didn't vanish. He followed them down the road. Whenever they peeked back, there he was, tapping his claws on the ground. How he laughed when the little cats scampered.

209

On they ran until they met a cow. "Where are you going so fast? On your way home from market, little cats?" asked the cow.

"The handre is chasing us," they gasped.

"I'll come with you," mooed the cow.

Next they met a dog, a crow, and a snake by the side of the path. "Why are you two cats and cow running so fast?" they asked.

"Because the handre is after us."

"We will help you," said the dog, the crow, and the snake. So they ran with the two little cats and the cow.

A little later they saw a pan of ashes, a box of needles, and a bowl of hard, dry peas. These things could talk, but they couldn't walk.

"You must be running away from the handre," said the peas.

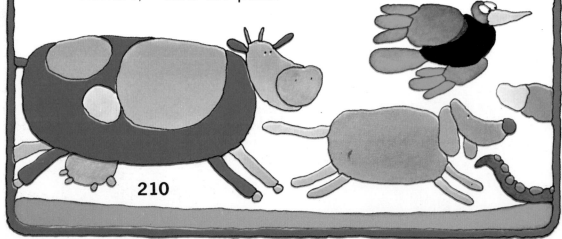

"Yes," whispered the cats. "And the cow, the dog, and the crow, and the snake are going home with us."

"Well, if you will carry us, we can help too." So the two little cats picked up the ashes, the needles, and the peas. They put them inside their shirts so they wouldn't drop them.

The handre was getting closer and closer, and the two little cats could hear his claws rattle.

"Hurry, hurry, lock the door," the cats cried.

Quickly the cow stood by the stairs. The dog got behind the door. The crow hid in the water barrel, and the snake curled up behind the bread. The two little cats put the pan of ashes above the door. They put the needles in the bed, and the peas rolled down the steps. The little cats put a blanket over their heads.

Sure enough, here came the handre. He found the door locked, so he just hopped in the window.

He rolled his eyes and rattled his claws and snarled. "Now I will really frighten those two little cats. Where are they ?"

He went to get a drink from the water barrel, and the crow pecked him. He tried to eat the bread, and the snake hissed at him. He went upstairs. He got under a blanket in the bed and the needles prickled. He looked up on top of the door, and the ashes sprinkled in his eyes.

As the handre started down the stairs, the hard peas rolled under his feet, and he fell on the hard horns of the cow. The cow tossed him lightly to the dog, who opened his mouth to bite him.

By that time the handre was frightened out of his rattles and snarls and had vanished completely. When the dog snapped his jaws, there was nothing there.

Finally the two little cats came out from under the blanket and thanked each of their friends for chasing away the handre. They all sat down and had some hot buttered tea, and they never, never saw the handre again.

The Donkey Egg

The Hodja lived in a small village with his wife, Fatima. They had one little donkey, and how they wished for one more donkey!

The Hodja had a friend, Ali. At times they had quarrels. Then they were not such good friends for a while. One day Ali brought a strange gift to the Hodja. From the folds of his loose coat, he brought it forth. It was large and smooth and round.

He offered the gift to the Hodja and Fatima. "A donkey egg," Ali said. "You must sit on this egg for three weeks. Then a baby donkey will hatch from it. He will grow and grow. In a few months, you will have another sturdy donkey. He can carry your loads to market. He can carry you where you want to go."

214

The Hodja was surprised. Just a week ago he and Ali had almost had a bad quarrel. Now his friend was helping them to have a second donkey.

"We thank you up to the heavens," the Hodja cried.

"And seven times above the heavens!" Fatima cried.

They kissed Ali's hand and pressed it to their foreheads. Over and over they thanked him.

The next three weeks were long ones. While the Hodja sat on the donkey egg, Fatima was busy. She fixed the meals, and cleaned the house, and twirled her spindle, and visited with the neighbor women.

While Fatima sat on the donkey egg, the Hodja went to market, and chopped wood, and talked with his friends in the coffee house.

Sitting on the donkey egg, the Hodja smoked his water pipe. He thought of wise advice to give his friends. He dreamed about the donkey.

Sitting on the donkey egg, Fatima twirled her hand spindle. She spun pounds and pounds of wool into scratchy yarn.

The neighbors came in to talk. The men came when the Hodja was sitting on the egg. The women came when they knew it was Fatima's turn to sit on it.

"Let us see the donkey egg," the women said. "We have never seen one."

"Oh, no," Fatima would reply. "We cannot let the egg get cold. We cannot take any chances." And so, no one but the Hodja and Fatima ever saw it.

216

A market day passed. A bath day passed. The first week was gone. The men went to the coffee house a second time. The people went to the public bath house a second time. And another week was gone. Then another market day and another bath day went by. Fatima had twirled her hand spindle for many hours. The third week was over.

At last it was time for the baby donkey to come out of the donkey egg. The Hodja tapped it. It was very soft. "Ah, yes," he said, "soon it will hatch."

So the Hodja and his wife took turns sitting on the donkey egg again. They sat for one more market day, and one more day at the public bath house. The egg grew even softer. But no baby donkey came out of it.

The egg did have a strange odor. It grew stronger as the egg grew softer. At last, the Hodja said to Fatima, "This egg is rotten. We cannot hope for our baby donkey any more."

He picked up the old donkey egg and put it under his arm. He walked slowly to the marketplace. All the people turned to look at him.

When his friends saw the egg, they nodded and smiled. The women looked at each other behind their veils. Then they looked at the Hodja and shook their heads. How strange everyone acted. The Hodja did not know why.

Children began to follow him. They were singing a silly chant. "*Donkey eggs grow on pumpkin vines,*" they chanted. They chanted it over and over. The Hodja was too sad to listen to the words. He went out of the town and climbed a hill.

218

At the top of the hill he stopped. He put the pumpkin on the ground. To the Hodja, the pumpkin was still a donkey egg. It started rolling down the hillside.

It rolled over rocks and around bushes. It rolled against a tree. It hit a stone and cracked open.

Under that tree a long-eared rabbit was sleeping. When the pumpkin burst open, the rabbit jumped up. He hopped off down the hill and out of sight.

It was a beautiful long-eared rabbit. The Hodja saw him. "Oh," he groaned. "The baby donkey at last! The donkey egg was just ready to hatch. *May heaven help us all,*" he shouted. "Now it has hatched and our baby donkey is lost forever!"

THE THREE SPINNING FAIRIES

Characters

ARDIS

STEPMOTHER

QUEEN

BROADFOOT

THICKTHUMB

GREATLIP

PRINCE

KING

SEVERAL WEDDING GUESTS

Act One

(*The inside of a small cottage.* ARDIS *sits before a small spinning wheel. Her* STEPMOTHER *paces about.*)

STEPMOTHER: No more excuses, you lazy girl! Get on with your spinning!

ARDIS: Dear Stepmother, please give me another task. May I milk the cow?

STEPMOTHER: You've already milked her. Have you forgotten? Now get on with your spinning!

ARDIS: The floor then, dear Stepmother. Let me wash the floor.

STEPMOTHER: Excuses! More excuses! You've scrubbed the floor twice already today. If you've forgotten, look about you. Now get spinning, you lazy girl!

(ARDIS *tries to spin, but the yarn tangles.*)

ARDIS: Oh, dear Stepmother, I've forgotten how to turn the wheel. Please may I do some baking—or some mending?

STEPMOTHER: You've already baked bread enough to last a week, and you've mended everything in sight! Now spin, you lazy thing, and get on with it!

221

ARDIS: Perhaps, dear Stepmother, if you would show me how—

STEPMOTHER (*grabbing a broom*): Show you! I'll show you! Lazy! Good-for-nothing!

(**ARDIS** *screams and dashes around the room, trying to keep away from the broom, as the* **QUEEN** *enters the room. When the* **STEPMOTHER** *sees the* **QUEEN**, *she drops the broom and stares.*)

QUEEN: My good woman, what is going on here? I heard screaming from the road as I drove past in my carriage.

STEPMOTHER: Oh, Your Majesty, it is my stepdaughter. She—she sits at that spinning wheel from dawn till dark. I am a poor woman, Your Majesty. I cannot afford to keep buying flax, and yet she will not stop spinning!

QUEEN: Good woman, let me take your daughter to the castle. I have enough flax, and she can spin as long as she likes.

STEPMOTHER: As you wish, Your Majesty, but I won't be surprised if you are soon as angry with her as I.

QUEEN: Nonsense! I am never happier than when I hear the sound of spinning. Come along, my girl.

223

Act Two

(*A room in the castle with a spinning wheel in the center and with bundles of flax piled everywhere. The* QUEEN *enters the room, leading* ARDIS.)

QUEEN: Here you are, my dear. Next door to this room are two more rooms just like it. Spin all this flax, and you shall have my son, the Prince, for your husband.

ARDIS: Your Majesty, I am only a poor girl, and—

QUEEN: My son has no need to marry a rich girl. A clever girl—that's the kind of wife he must have. Now I know you are happy to spend your time doing what you love best, so I will leave you and come back tomorrow.

(QUEEN *leaves.* ARDIS *paces about.*)

ARDIS: What shall I do? I've tried and tried, but I've just never been able to learn to spin.

(ARDIS *sits at the spinning wheel, but soon the flax is a huge tangle.*)

ARDIS: Oh, it is hopeless! The Queen will surely think I am lazy. What can I do!

(ARDIS *begins to cry.* BROADFOOT, THICKTHUMB, *and* GREATLIP *enter.* BROADFOOT *has one very large foot.* THICKTHUMB *has one thumb as large as a man's hand.* GREATLIP'S *lower lip sticks out several inches past her nose.*)

225

BROADFOOT: There, there, Ardis. Do not weep.

ARDIS: Who are you? And how do you know my name?

BROADFOOT: I am Broadfoot, and these are my sisters, Thickthumb, and Greatlip. We know many things, and we have come to help you.

GREATLIP: Yes, to help you.

ARDIS: You are very kind, but I am afraid no one can help me. Why, I could never spin this flax in a hundred years, even if I knew how to spin.

THICKTHUMB: That is why we are here.

226

BROADFOOT: We can spin this flax into yarn before morning.

THICKTHUMB: And we'll be glad to do it. We love to spin.

GREATLIP: Yes, we love to spin !

ARDIS: But how could I ever repay you ?

THICKTHUMB: We ask no pay. Just invite us to the wedding, so that we may share your joy.

BROADFOOT: And at the wedding, so that we may sit by you at the family table, you must introduce us as your cousins.

ARDIS: Oh, I'll gladly invite you to the wedding. And you are so kind I truly wish you were my cousins.

THICKTHUMB: Very well, then. Let's get on with our spinning.

GREATLIP: Yes, on with our spinning !

Act Three

(*The same room very early the next morning. Yarn now fills the whole room.* **BROADFOOT** *and* **THICKTHUMB** *and* **GREATLIP** *stand looking at the yarn.* **ARDIS** *stares and stares.*)

ARDIS: I can hardly believe it. To think that all three rooms are done!

BROADFOOT: Well, we are finished. Soon the Queen will return, so we must be going.

GREATLIP: Yes, we must be going!

ARDIS: Oh, my dear friends, I can never thank you.

THICKTHUMB: No need to thank us, Ardis. Just be a good wife to the Prince, and don't forget your promise.

GREATLIP: Yes, don't forget your promise!

(**BROADFOOT**, **GREATLIP**, *and* **THICKTHUMB** *exit. Then the* **QUEEN** *enters and stares about her.*)

QUEEN: I can't believe my eyes! Come, we will get you some food, and then you must rest before you begin on the other two rooms.

ARDIS: Thank you, Your Majesty, but the flax in all three rooms is spun.

QUEEN: I am at a loss for words!

ARDIS: I am happy if you are pleased, Your Majesty.

QUEEN: My dear, I am overjoyed! You are, indeed, a clever girl and the wife for the Prince. Come, we will announce the coming wedding throughout the Kingdom.

ARDIS: May I ask one favor, Your Majesty?

QUEEN: Of course. Anything you wish!

ARDIS: I have three dear cousins who have been very kind to me in the past. May I invite them to the wedding?

QUEEN: You may invite anyone you wish. Now come. There is much to be done this happy day.

Act Four

(*The great hall of the castle.* ARDIS *and the* PRINCE *stand arm in arm. The* KING *and* QUEEN *greet guests who enter and leave.* BROADFOOT, THICKTHUMB *and* GREATLIP *enter. Everyone turns to stare but* ARDIS, *who rushes to greet them. The* PRINCE *follows, staring.*)

ARDIS: Dear cousins, I am so glad you could come !

BROADFOOT: How beautiful you look, my dear, and how happy.

THICKTHUMB: Now pay no attention to us, Ardis. We'll just mingle and enjoy ourselves. It was kind of you to invite us.

GREATLIP: Yes, it was kind of you to invite us !

(*The Three go to greet the* KING *and* QUEEN. *The* PRINCE *leads* ARDIS *to one side, away from the others.*)

230

PRINCE: Those three women—did you say they were your cousins?

ARDIS: Yes, and three more wonderful cousins I could never hope to have!

PRINCE: I'm sure they are very nice. Still, it does seem odd.

ARDIS: Odd? I don't understand.

PRINCE: I mean, my dear, that you are so beautiful, and to be quite truthful, I have never seen three more ugly-looking women.

ARDIS: I'm happy that you think me beautiful, dear Husband. And I'm sure that when you get to know my cousins, you will have forgotten their strange looks.

231

(**KING** *and* **QUEEN** *approach and lead* **ARDIS** *away as the* **KING** *speaks.*)

KING: Come, my dear. You must meet more of the guests.

(*The* **PRINCE** *walks about from one fairy to another, staring. They do not seem to notice. At last he leads* **BROADFOOT** *to the front of the stage.*)

PRINCE: Pardon me, Cousin, but I cannot help staring at your foot.

BROADFOOT: Oh, many people stare at my foot. It is very broad.

PRINCE: I hope you won't mind if I ask how it came to be so.

BROADFOOT: Not at all, Your Highness. Once my foot was as slim as that of my cousin, Ardis. Everyone in our family loves to spin, you know. And when one spins, one turns the wheel.

PRINCE: You turn the wheel with your foot?

BROADFOOT: Oh, yes! I can turn the wheel faster than anyone in the family.

PRINCE: I see. Yes, I see.

(*The* PRINCE *leaves* BROADFOOT *and brings* THICKTHUMB *to the front of the stage.*)

PRINCE: Excuse me, Cousin, but I cannot help staring at your thumb.

THICKTHUMB: Oh I am quite used to it. After all, not many have such a thumb.

PRINCE: I hope you won't mind my asking how it came to be so.

THICKTHUMB: I am happy to tell you, Your Highness. Once my thumb was quite ordinary—much like that of Ardis, your lovely bride. Our family, you know, is known for its spinners, and with this thumb I twist thread faster than anyone.

233

PRINCE: Twisting the thread made your thumb thick ?

THICKTHUMB: Yes, and now I have a thumb that is really something !

PRINCE: Yes. Yes, indeed !

(PRINCE *leaves* THICKTHUMB *and brings* GREATLIP *to the front of the stage.*)

PRINCE: I hope, dear Cousin, that you won't think me rude, but it is hard not to notice your unusual lower lip.

GREATLIP: Yes, I have an unusual lower lip !

PRINCE: Tell me, has spinning made it so ?

GREATLIP: Yes, spinning has made it so. I moisten the thread ! I moisten the thread !

(*The* PRINCE *leaves* GREATLIP *and goes to* ARDIS.)

PRINCE: My dear, I have something to ask of you.

ARDIS: How can I refuse my husband anything on our wedding day?

PRINCE: I have talked to your cousins, and I know how much spinning means to your family. Still, it is my wish that my beautiful wife not touch a spinning wheel again! Can you bear to give up spinning, my dear?

ARDIS: (*smiling at the Three, and then turning back to the* **PRINCE**): For your sake, my love, I will do just that!

The Habits of the Hippopotamus

The hippopotamus is strong
  And huge of head and broad of bustle;
The limbs on which he rolls along
  Are big with hippopotomuscle.

He does not greatly care for sweets
  Like ice cream, apple pie, or custard,
But takes to flavor what he eats
  A little hippopotomustard.

The hippopotamus is true
  To all his principles, and just;
He always tries his best to do
  The things one hippopotomust.

He never rides in trucks or trams,
  In taxicabs or omnibuses,
And so keeps out of traffic jams
  and other hippopotomusses.

Arthur Guiterman

THE HOUSE OF THE SUN

(A Legend of the Hawaiian Islands)

A long time ago, islands were pushed up from the sea. The heavens were spread over them. Light reached them, and people were living on them.

At that time the great Maui lived on one of the islands. He was strong and clever. He had already put the heavens in their place. Many people thought he was a god.

The Sun was very helpful too, because he brought light and warmth. But the Sun ran too fast across the heavens. There was not enough light for each day. The people could never finish their work before dark. Plants could not grow tall and strong.

One day Maui sat watching his mother, Hina, at work. She was making tapa cloth from the bark of trees. It took her a long time to pound the bark into thin strips. It took a long time to paste the wet strips together. And then it took more time for them to dry and become tapa cloth.

The hurrying Sun did not give Hina time enough to finish her work. And in those days, tapa was the only cloth the people had. Maui decided to do something about this.

"I will trick the Sun and make him behave himself," he told his mother.

Maui climbed to a high place where he could watch the Sun. This was the crater of an old dead volcano. Here he watched the Sun rise and pass over the mountain.

Maui made a plan. He would snare the Sun and cut off his legs. Then the Sun could not move so fast and the days would be longer.

Maui told his mother what he was going to do. She gave him fifteen lengths of very strong rope to use in snaring the Sun. But that was not enough.

"Go now to your old grandmother who lives in the great crater," Hina said. "She will give you whatever else you need."

"How can that be?" asked Maui.

His mother said, "Climb the mountain to the place where the great wiliwili tree stands. Every day the Sun stops there to eat the bananas that your grandmother cooks for him." But that was not all.

"Wait by the tree," his mother went on, "until your grandmother comes to make her fire. Tell her you are Hina's son."

Maui did as his mother told him. Because his grandmother was almost blind, she did not see him. But she began to sniff around. Then she knew that someone was near.

"Who are you?" she cried.

"I am your grandson, Maui," he called. "I am Hina's son." Then he told her how he was going to catch the Sun by his sixteen legs and punish him for the way he treated the people.

"I will help you," said the old woman. She gave him one more rope so that he could catch the last leg of the Sun with it. And she gave him a magic stone to use as a battle-axe.

"Make a hiding-place for yourself by the wiliwili tree," she said. "When the first leg of the Sun creeps over the mountainside, snare it with a rope. Do this to each leg until you have caught all sixteen. Then tie them tightly to the wiliwili tree. Use the magic stone in your battle with the Sun."

Maui obeyed. When the first leg of the Sun came over the east rim of the crater, Maui quickly snared it. One after another, as each leg crept over the rim, he snared it.

Finally he had snared fifteen, and only one leg still clung to the mountainside. At last it came up over the edge of the mountain. Then Maui snared that leg too with the rope his grandmother had given him.

The Sun tried to slip down the mountainside and back into the sea. But Maui had tied the ropes to the great wiliwili tree. The ropes held the Sun where he was.

Maui took his magic stone and struck at the Sun with all his might. He struck and struck until the Sun begged for his life.

"If I let you live," said Maui, "will you think of the people on Earth? Will you remember to help them get their work done?"

They talked for a long time. At last they reached an agreement. Some days the Sun would move slowly and take a long time to cross the sky. Then the days would be longer. The people would be able to finish their work. At other times the Sun could go faster. Then the days would be shorter. The people would not work so hard on these days.

The longer days would be called *summer,* and the shorter days *winter.*

This was the agreement. Now Hina could finish her tapa cloth. Fishermen could catch enough fish. Plants could give the people more food.

Maui let the Sun go. Some say that he left the ropes by the wiliwili tree. Then the Sun would see them each day when he came over the mountain, and remember.

From that day to this, the mountain has been known as Ha-le-a-ka-la, the House of the Sun.

Make Your Own Story

Now that you know more about folk tales, here are some characters for your very own tale.

King Bong is a wicked man. He is greedy and selfish. Yet he wants the people in his kingdom to like him.

Princess Rose, King Bong's daughter, is very sad. She likes the people in the kingdom and helps them whenever she can. The people like her very much.

Wug is the son of the village shoemaker. He helps his father in the shop and often runs errands to the castle.

Remember the way in which the story of "The Three Spinning Fairies" was told. The fairies helped Ardis with her problem. Thinking about how that story begins and ends may help you use the three new characters in telling your own folk tale.

Playing a Story Game

Follow the trail to the castle. Name each story as you come to a picture

245

CHARLIE THE TRAMP[1]

by RUSSELL HOBAN   Pictures by LILLIAN HOBAN

"Well, well," said Grandfather Beaver one day when he came to visit, "Charlie is getting to be a big boy."

"Yes, he is," said Father. "He is coming right along."

Grandfather smiled at Charlie and took a quarter out of his vest pocket.

"What are you going to be when you grow up, Charlie?" asked Grandfather.

"I am going to be a tramp," said Charlie.

"A tramp!" said Mother.

"A tramp!" said Father.

"A tramp!" said Grandfather, and he put
the quarter back in his vest pocket.

"Yes," said Charlie, "I am going to be a
tramp."

"I am surprised to hear that," said
Father. "Your grandfather has been doing
beaver work for many years, and I too am a
beaver, but you want to be a tramp."

"That is how it is now-a-days," said
Grandfather, shaking his head. "When I was
young, children did not want to be tramps."

"I don't think Charlie really wants to be
a tramp," said Mother.

"Yes, I do," said Charlie. "Tramps don't
have to learn how to chop down trees and
how to roll logs and how to build dams.

"Tramps don't have to practice swimming and diving and holding their breath under water.

"Nobody looks to see if their teeth are sharp. Nobody looks to see if their fur is oiled.

"Tramps carry sticks with little bundles tied to them. They sleep in a field when the weather is nice, and when it rains they sleep in a barn.

"Tramps just tramp around and have a good time. And when they want something to eat, they do little jobs for anybody that wants little jobs done."

"I have lots of little jobs for you to do,"
said Father. "You can help me cut saplings
for our winter food. You can help me dig
extra tunnels for our lodge. And of course
the dam always needs repairs."

"That is not little jobs," said Charlie. "That's hard work."

"When I was young," said Grandfather, "children did hard work. Now-a-days all they want to do is little jobs."

"Well," said Father, "if Charlie wants to be a tramp, then I think he should be a tramp. I think we should not stand in his way."

"The weather is nice and warm now," said Charlie. "May I start sleeping in fields?"

"All right," said Mother.

Charlie tied up some fig newtons and some Good-and-Plenties in a handkerchief. Then he tied the handkerchief to a stick and he was ready to go.

"Now it is time for me to be on the road and away," said Charlie.

"Good-bye, Mr. Tramp," said Father and Grandfather.

"Good-bye, Mr. Tramp," said Mother. "Come home in time for breakfast, and don't forget to brush your teeth tonight."

"Good-bye," said Charlie. "Tramps don't brush their teeth."

He got into his little boat, rowed across the pond, and tramped off down the road, while Mother and Father and Grandfather waved to him.

"Now that I think of it," said Grandfather, "I wanted to be a tramp when I was little, just like Charlie."

"So did I," said Father.

"That is how men are," said Mother. "They all want to be tramps."

Charlie tramped down the road, kicking a stone and whistling a tramping song as he went.

He looked at the blue hills far away, and he listened to cowbells tinkling in distant meadows.

Sometimes he stopped to throw stones at telephone poles, and sometimes he sat under a tree and watched the clouds roll by.

Charlie kept tramping until it was almost sundown, and then he picked a field to sleep in. He picked a field where daisies grew, and the grass and the clover smelled sweet.

Charlie untied his little bundle and took out some fig newtons and some Good-and-Plenties, and he ate them while the stars came out.

"Being a tramp is nice," said Charlie to himself, and he went to sleep.

Mother was watching for him at the window the next morning when he rowed across the pond.

"Here comes Charlie," she said to Father, "with his fur every which way and a bundle of daisies on his stick."

"Good morning, Lady," said Charlie when Mother opened the door. And he gave her the daisies. "Do you have a little job I can do for my breakfast?" he said.

"You can bail out the big rowboat," said Father. "That will be a nice little job for you."

"All right," said Charlie. "And then I will eat my breakfast on the back steps, because that is how we tramps do it."

So Charlie bailed out the rowboat. And
while he was eating his breakfast on the
back steps, Father came and sat down
beside him. "How do you like being a
tramp?" he said.

"I like it fine," said Charlie. "It is a lot
easier than being a beaver."

"How did you sleep last night?" said
Father.

"Fine," said Charlie. "But something kept
waking me up."

"Was it anything scary?" said Father.

"No," said Charlie, "it was something
nice, but I don't know what it was. I will
have to listen for it again tonight."

Then Charlie rowed across the pond and
went off down the road, whistling his
tramping song.

Charlie tramped all day.
He listened to the birds singing.
He smelled the flowers that grew by the side
of the road. Sometimes he stopped to pick
blackberries. Sometimes he walked along the
top rails of fences.

At lunch time and dinner time Charlie went home and did little jobs for his lunch and his dinner.

He stacked winter saplings in the basement for his lunch. And for his dinner he helped his father fix a broken plank in the boat landing.

After dinner, Charlie went back to the field where the clover and the daisies grew. Charlie ate his fig newtons and his Good-and-Plenties, and he listened for the sound he had heard the night before.

Charlie heard the frogs and the crickets singing in the quiet of the night, and he heard something else. He heard a trickling, tickling kind of a little song that had no words.

The trickling, tickling song made Charlie want to hear it better. So he got up and went down to the trees where the sound was coming from.

He saw a little stream that sang as it ran in the moonlight, and he sat down and listened to the song again. But the sound of the trickling kept tickling Charlie, and he could not sit still.

So he took off his clothes, and he dived into the stream and swam around inside the song the water was singing.

Then Charlie climbed out and cut down a little tree that was growing on the bank. When the tree fell down, he rolled it into the water.

Charlie took a deep breath and swam to the bottom of the stream with the tree and stuck it in the mud so that it would not float away.

Then he listened to the song of the water,
and he liked it better than he had before.
So Charlie cut down some more trees, and
he began to make a little dam to keep all

the water from trickling away.

Charlie worked on his dam all night. And
by morning the stream had widened into a
pond. Then the song of the water stopped
tickling Charlie, and he said, "Now I guess
I can go back to sleep."

So he brushed his teeth to keep them sharp. He oiled his fur to keep it waterproof. And he went to sleep in an old hollow tree by his new pond.

Charlie slept right through breakfast time, and Mother began to worry when she did not see him.

"I am sure Charlie is all right," said Father, "but I think we should look for him anyhow." And he went down to the boat landing and slapped the water with his tail, WHACK!

WHACK! answered Grandfather with his tail, and he came over to see what was the matter.

"I never did think any good would come of letting that boy run off to be a tramp," said Mother.

"That's how it is now-a-days," said Grandfather. "Boys run off, and no good comes of it."

So Mother and Father and Grandfather went looking for Charlie, and after a while they came to the new pond. But they did not see Charlie sleeping in the hollow tree.

"I don't remember seeing a pond around
here before," said Grandfather.

"Neither do I," said Father. "It must be
a new one."

"That's a pretty good pond," said Grandfather. "I wonder who made it?"

"I don't know," said Father. "You think maybe Harry Beaver might have done it?"

"No," said Grandfather. "Harry always makes a sloppy dam, and this one's not sloppy at all."

"What about old Zeb Beaver?" said Father. "Zeb always makes a good-looking dam."

"No," said Grandfather. "Zeb never makes a round pond like this one. Zeb always likes a long-shaped pond."

"You're right," said Father. "He does."

"You know," said Mother to Father, "this pond looks like the ponds you make."

"She's right," said Grandfather. "It does."

"That's funny," said Father. "I didn't make it. I wonder who did?"

276

"I did," said Charlie, waking up and coming out of the hollow tree. "That's my pond."

"That's your pond?" said Father.
"That's my pond," said Charlie.

"I thought you were a tramp," said Grandfather. "Tramps don't make ponds."

"Well," said Charlie, "sometimes I like to tramp around, and sometimes I like to make ponds."

"Any tramp that can make a pond like that is going to be some beaver one of these days," said Father.

"That's how it is now-a-days," said
Grandfather. "You never know when a tramp
will turn out to be a beaver." And he took
the quarter out of his vest pocket and gave
it to Charlie.

Key to Pronunciation

Letter Symbol for a sound	Key Word and Its Respelling	Letter Symbol for a sound	Key Word and Its Respelling
a	pat (PAT)	ch	church (CHERCH)
ah	far (FAHR)	hw	when (HWEN)
ai	air (AIR)	ks	mix (MIKS)
aw	jaw (JAW)	kw	quick (KWIK)
ay	pay (PAY)	ng	thing (THING)
e	pet (PET)		finger (FING-gər)
ee	bee (BEE)	sh	shoe (SHOO)
ehr	berry (BEHR-ee)	ss	case (KAYSS)
er	term (TERM)	th	thing (THING)
i	pit (PIT)	th	this (THIS)
igh	sigh (SIGH)	zh	pleasure (PLEZH-ər)
ihr	pier (PIHR)		
o	pot (POT)		
oh	oh, boat (BOHT)		
oi	oil (OIL)		
oo	boot, rule (ROOL)		
or	for (FOR)		
ow	power (POW-ər)		
u	put, book (BUK)		
uh	cut (KUHT)		

y	used in place of (igh) before two consonant letters as in child (CHYLD)
ə	represents the sound for any vowel spelling when a syllable is sounded very weakly, as in the first syllable of *about*, or the last syllables of *item*, *gallop*, or *focus*, or the middle syllable of *charity*

Glossary

a·ble (AY-bəl) 1. Having the skill, power or understanding to do something: Raccoons are *able* to climb trees. 2. Skillful: The violinist is an *able* musician; he plays well. **abler, ablest.**

ad·vice (ad-VIGHSS) What one person may tell another person about the way something should be done: My doctor's *advice* was for me to get more rest and sleep.

The pronunciation system and word entries are adapted from *The Ginn Intermediate Dictionary*, published by Ginn and Company (A Xerox Education Company). Copyright © 1973 by Xerox Corporation.

be·hold·en (bi-HOHL-dn) Having to pay or give something to another because of a promise or kindness received: They were *beholden* to the farmer for his help.

be·wil·der (bi-WIL-dər) To mix up a person's thoughts: That puzzle will surely *bewilder* my sister.

blan·ket (BLANG-kit) 1. A large, warm covering; a bed cover for a sleeping person. 2. A covering; something like a bed cover: The ground was covered with a *blanket* of snow. 3. To cover: Fallen leaves *blanket* our yard. **blanketed, blanketing.**

breath (BRETH) 1. Air taken in and out of the lungs. 2. The moisture or vapor carried out with air from the lungs: On a cold day you can see your *breath*. 3. Power, spirit, life, or time: We'll save our *breath* for the hard work. 4. A rest: Let me take a *breath* before we go on.

bright 1. Shining with light: The sun is very *bright* today. 2. Smart, clever: That was a very *bright* idea. 3. Happy: The *bright,* laughing group made their way to the beach. 4. Clear or strong: The *bright* red of Sally's dress made her seem to glow. **brighter, brightest, brightly.**

cas·tle (KASS-l) 1. A very large building, usually with thick walls and round high towers. 2. A large home that looks like a castle. 3. One of the pieces in a chess game.

cer·tain (SERT-n) 1. Sure: I am *certain* that he is not home. 2. Some: Tim dislikes *certain* foods. 3. Special: There is one *certain* dog on my street that bites. **certainly.**

clump (KLUHMP) 1. A solid mass; a lump: a *clump* of mud. 2. A group of things close together: a *clump* of bushes. 3. A dull thud; the sound of heavy footsteps. 4. To walk with heavy footsteps. **clumped, clumping.**

cov·er (KUHV-ər) 1. To put something over or on in order to hide or keep safe: Please *cover* your schoolbooks. 2. To blanket: The leaves *cover* the grass. 3. To dress; put on clothes: *Cover* your head in the rain. 4. Anything that covers, as a lid, a hat, a blanket. **covered, covering.**

cra·ter (KRAY-tər) 1. The hollowed-out opening at the top of a volcano. 2. Any cup-like opening formed by nature or by the crash of a meteor or bomb.

crys·tal (KRISS-tl) 1. A kind of glass that is clear: Some drinking glasses are made of *crystal*. 2. The glass over the face of a watch. 3. A shape with many sides all the same: a snow *crystal*. 4. Clear: The water is *crystal* clear.

di·rec·tion (də-REK-shən) 1. The act of leading: We work under the teacher's *direction*. 2. The way to which something faces or moves; north, south, east, west. 3. Something that tells someone what to do: Follow the *directions* on the box.

ex·er·cise (EK-sər-sighz) 1. An activity that makes the body strong: Running is a good *exercise.* 2. An activity that helps you learn something: We have a spelling *exercise* for homework. **exercised, exercising.**

for·ward (FOR-wərd) 1. Ahead, toward the front: The train moved *forward* slowly. 2. Toward the goal of the other team: He threw a *forward* pass. 3. To send on: Please *forward* the mail to our new address. **forwarded, forwarding.**

foun·tain (FOWNT-n)
1. A spring of water bubbling from the earth; the start of a stream. 2. A stream of water that goes up in the air: Where is the drinking *fountain?*
3. The shooting sprays of water that are used for decoration.

fume (FYOOM) 1. To send out terrible smelling vapors, odors, gas, or smoke: The fire will *fume* if you don't put it out well. 2. Terrible smelling smoke, vapors, gases, or odors: The *fumes* from the bus made us sick. **fumed, fuming.**

gla·cier (GLAY-shər)
A large mass of ice, formed from snow that is slowly moving down mountain slopes.

grain (GRAYN) 1. The seeds of certain food plant such as corn, wheat, rice, or oats. 2. The way the fibers are placed in meat, wood, or cloth: Sew the cloth in the direction of the *grain.* 3. A very small piece: *grains* of sand.

great (GRAYT) 1. Large in size; big: a *great* mob of people. 2. Fine, very good: *great* men, *great* books, a *great* person. **greater, greatest, greatly.**

hol·low (HOL-oh) 1. Not solid; having a hole on the inside: a *hollow* pipe. 2. Curved inward: *hollow* cheeks. 3. An empty place; a hole. 4. To make hollow: Can you *hollow* out this log? **hollowed, hollowing.**

humming bird A very, very small brightly-colored bird with a long bill and thin wings. While in flight its wings make a soft humming-like sound.

ice·berg (IGHSS-bərg)
A mass of ice broken away from a glacier and floating in the ocean.

in·ter·rupt (in-tə-RUHPT) 1. To cause to stop for a short time: We will have to *interrupt* the meeting for a one-hour break for lunch. 2. To break in upon the speech or actions of another: It was rude of Ralph to *interrupt* our guest speaker. **interrupted, interrupting.**

284

join   1. To bring together: *join* two ropes.   2. To become a member: Can you *join* our club?   3. To become a part of: Everyone can *join* for this song. **joined, joining.**

jut   (JUHT)   To stick out. **jutted.**

la·bel   (LAY-bəl)   1. A piece of paper or tag that tells about the thing on which it is placed: The *label* on the bottle says that it is poison.   2. To place a label on: Father will *label* the jars. **labeled** or **labelled, labeling** or **labelling.**

les·son   (LESS-n)   1. Something that is taught: a spelling *lesson.*   2. Anything learned: Bob learned a *lesson* when he cut his finger.

liq·uid   (LIK-wid)   1. Something like water that is able to flow and change into the shape of whatever holds it.   2. Melted: Pour *liquid* butter over the popcorn.

mar·ket   (MAHR-kit)   1. A store, usually where just one kind of food is sold: vegetable *market.*   2. A place where goods are bought and sold: The farmers bring their goods to *market* on Saturdays.   3. To shop; buy food: Sally often *markets* for her mother. **marketed, marketing.**

nee·dle   (NEED-l)   1. A thin piece of steel with a hole at one end and sharp point at the other end used for sewing.   2. A thin leaf, as on an evergreen tree. **needles.**

no·tice   (NOH-tiss)   1. A written or printed announcement: a *notice* on the bulletin board.   2. To see or pay attention to: Did you *notice* the nice clothes in that store? **notices, noticed, noticing.**

oc·to·pus   (OK-tə-pəss)   A sea animal that has a soft body and eight long arms which are covered with suckers. **octopuses** or **octopi.**

o·dor   (OH-dər)   A scent or smell: the *odor* of flowers.

plead   (PLEED)   1. To ask for; beg: John always *pleads* to stay up and watch TV.   2. To give as an excuse: *Plead* sickness for not going to the meeting.   3. To argue for or against, as in a courtroom. *plead* a case. **pleaded** or **pled, pleading.**

polar bear   A large white bear found where it is cold, as in the North Pole.

pol·lute   (pə-LOOT)   To make something dirty: Many factories *pollute* the air. **polluted, polluting.**

¹**pound**   (POWND)   A weight equal to 16 ounces.

²**pound**   (POWND)   1. To hit again and again: *Pound* the nail with the hammer.   2. To beat heavily: I could feel my heart *pound* after the long run. **pounded, pounding.**

³**pound**   (POWND)   A public place for keeping stray animals.

pump·kin (PUHMP-kin or PUHNG-kin)
1. A very large orange-colored fruit of the squash family.
2. An orange color.

rat·tle·snake (RAT-l-snayk)
A poisonous snake that has hard rings that rattle at the end of its tail. **rattlesnakes.**

res·er·va·tion (rez-ər-VAY-shən)
1. A piece of land set apart by the United States government for a special use.
2. Something held for a person: Phil had a *reservation* for a seat at the game.

rus·tle (RUHSS-l)
1. To make a soft, crackling sound like that made by leaves in the wind: Did you hear something *rustle* in the bushes?
2. To steal livestock: The thieves *rustled* 30 cows from the ranch. **rustled, rustling.**

scat·ter (SKAT-ər)
1. To spread around; sprinkle: *scatter* seeds.
2. To move away, or cause to move away, in different directions: As the truck came down the street, I saw the boys *scatter*. **scattered, scattering.**

scent (SENT)
1. Odor, smell: The *scent* of roses came from the garden.
2. Perfume: Wendy likes her lilac *scent* the best.
3. Sense of smell: Hunting dogs must have a sharp *scent*.
4. To smell: The dogs *scent* the deer. **scented, scenting.**

sci·ence (SIGH-ənss) The skill or art of learning by watching, testing, and thinking about nature in an orderly way: We learned about frogs in *science* class.

sci·en·tist (SIGH-ən-tist) A person that finds facts by watching, testing, and thinking.

¹scrap (SKRAP)
1. A small piece; a bit: Tom tore a *scrap* from the corner of the paper.
2. Bits of food left over: We gave the dog *scraps* from dinner. **scraps.**

²scrap (SKRAP) A fight or quarrel: The boys had a *scrap* over which program to watch. **scrapped, scrapping.**

sense (SENSS)
1. A feeling: a *sense* of fear.
2. Ability to understand or think: common *sense*.
3. The ability to know things about oneself: Our five *senses* are sight, hearing, taste, smell, and touch.
4. Meaning: the *sense* of the word.
5. To feel: I can *sense* something is wrong. **senses, sensed, sensing.**

sigh
1. To let out a long deep breath, usually when one is sad, tired, or happy.
2. The sound of sighing. **sighed, sighing.**

sky·rock·et (SKY-rok-it)
A firework that can burst into bright sparks after being shot into the sky.

sleek
1. Shiny and smooth: The seal's coat was very *sleek*.
2. To make neat or smooth. **sleeked, sleeking, sleekness.**

sol·id (SOL-id) 1. Firm; hard: Some melons were *solid,* but others were soft. 2. Not in the form of liquid or gas: Ice is water in a *solid* form. 3. Not hollow: My candy egg is hollow, but Jan's is *solid* chocolate. 4. Firm and stiff, strong, well-built: The shaky old house was not very *solid.*

spe·cial (SPESH-əl) 1. Certain, different: This is a *special* kind of plant. 2. Made or planned for one person or reason: We can send this letter by *special* mail. 3. Apart from others, belonging to: Coin collecting is his *special* hobby. 4. Something that is different from the usual, such as a sale or a TV show. **specially.**

spice (SPYSS) 1. A plant with a pleasing, strong smell or taste, used to give a special taste to food: Pepper is a *spice.* 2. To add spice to: Father should *spice* up the stew. **spices, spiced, spicing, spicy.**

sprin·kle (SPRING-kəl) 1. To scatter in little bits or drops: *Sprinkle* some salt. 2. To rain a little bit. 3. A small amount: Give the soup just a *sprinkle* of salt. **sprinkled, sprinkling.**

sput·ter (SPUHT-ər) 1. To make hissing, spitting noises: I heard the car *sputter* down the street. 2. To talk in a way that is hard to understand: Mary started to *sputter* while reading her report. **sputtered, sputtering.**

straight (STRAYT) 1. Not bent or curved: I can't draw a *straight* line. 2. In a line; in order: The desks were *straight* when class began. 3. Not bending or tipping: Stand *straight.* **straighter.**

strike (STRIGHK) 1. Hit. 2. To sound: I heard the clock *strike* two. 3. To swing the bat at and miss a pitched ball. 4. To make burn by rubbing: *Strike* a match. **struck, striking.**

stur·dy (STER-dee) 1. Strong; well-built: Is this ladder *sturdy* enough? 2. Healthy: John is a very *sturdy* young man. **sturdier, sturdiest, sturdiness, sturdily.**

tan·gle (TANG-gəl) 1. To mix together so that it is hard to get apart: The wind will *tangle* my hair. 2. A mixed-up mess: Bill's clothes were in a *tangle* on the bed. **tangled, tangling.**

¹**tear** (TIHR) 1. A drop of salty liquid from the eye: A *tear* fell from his eye. 2. To become full of tears. **teared, tearing.**

²**tear** (TAIR) 1. To rip into pieces 2. To hurt or harm as by catching on something. 3. The hole caused by tearing: The *tear* in his jeans was huge. **tore, tearing.**

touch (TUHCH) 1. To feel; to press lightly against: Don't *touch* the hot stove. 2. The ability to sense through the fingers or other body parts what something feels like: Blind people depend on their sense of *touch.* **touched, touching.**

tour (TUR) 1. Going from place to place: They were *touring* their parents through the school. 2. To make a trip: Would you like to *tour* Canada? **toured, touring.**

tow·er (TOW-ər) 1. A high, thin building or such a part of a building: The bells are in the church *tower*. 2. To stand high or tall: John and Joe *tower* over Bob. **towered, towering.**

trem·ble (TREM-bəl) 1. To shiver; shake with fear, cold, or weakness: The little kitten started to *tremble* when I picked it up. 2. To shake: When big heavy trucks pass, it makes the house *tremble*. **trembled, trembling.**

tube (TOOB or TYOOB) 1. A long, hollow, pipe-like thing made of rubber, metal, paper, or glass: Paper towels are wrapped around a *tube* of cardboard. 2. A tube-shaped holder: Toothpaste and oil paints come in *tubes*. 3. A part for a radio or TV set. 4. Rubber air-filled casing used inside some automobile tires. **tubes.**

tuft (TUHFT) A small bunch of threads, feathers, hair, or such held together at one end or growing closely together. **tufted, tufting.**

twirl (TWERL) 1. To turn round and round quickly and lightly: spin. 2. To turn suddenly and face the other direction. 3. To twist or twine around: Please don't *twirl* your hair. **twirled, twirling, twirler.**

van·ish (VAN-ish) 1. To drop out of sight: The dew will *vanish* when the sun comes out. 2. To die out; stop living: Many wild animals may *vanish* if we don't try to save them.

va·por (VAY-pər) 1. Smoke or moisture hanging in the air: Fog is water *vapor*. 2. A gas formed by heating a liquid: *vapor* from a kettle.

veil (VAYL) 1. A piece of very fine cloth like a net, worn by some women over the head, sometimes hiding the face. 2. To cover with a veil: Clouds *veil* the sun. **veiled, veiling.**

wan·der (WON-dər) To move around with no plan: The sheep *wander* around the meadow. **wandered, wandering, wanderer.**

zig·zag (ZIG-zag) 1. A line or path that moves in a back and forth motion with sharp turns and angles: The letter Z is a *zigzag* letter. 2. To move with or make many sharp turns: The dogs saw the deer *zigzag* through the woods. **zigzagged, zigzagging.**

BCDEFGHIJK 79876
PRINTED IN THE UNITED STATES OF AMERICA